Buckle Down™

California Mathematics Level 2

2nd Edition

This book belongs to: ______________________________

Helping your schoolhouse meet the standards of the statehouse™

ISBN-10: 0-7836-5271-2
ISBN-13: 978-0-7836-5271-9

2BDCA02MM01 9 10

Senior Editor: Paul Meyers; Project Editor: Lynn Tauro; Editor: Tanya Burken; Production Editor: Jennifer Rapp; Cover Design: Christina Nantz; Cover Graphic Designer: Christina Kroemer; Production Director: Jennifer Booth; Art Director: Chris Wolf; Graphic Designer: Spike Schabacker; Composition: Wyndham Books.

TABLE OF CONTENTS

To the Teacher:

Content Standards numbers are listed for each lesson in the table of contents. The numbers in the shaded gray bar that runs across the tops of the pages in the workbook indicate the Content Standards for a given page (see example to the right). The example below shows what each part of the code stands for.

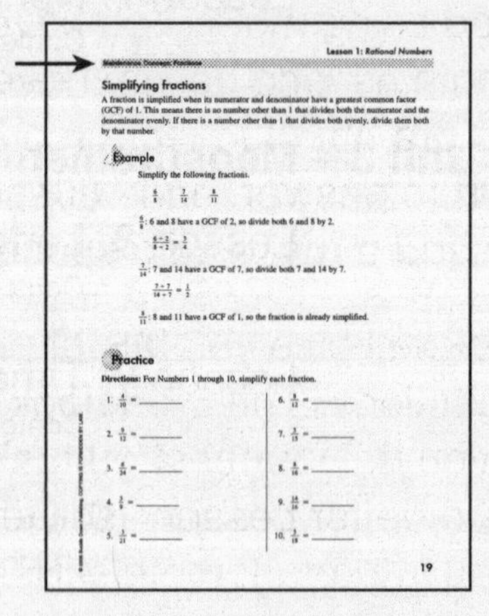

Lesson 1: *Rational Numbers*

Simplifying fractions

A fraction is simplified when its numerator and denominator have a greatest common factor (GCF) of 1. This means there is no number other than 1 that divides both the numerator and the denominator evenly. If there is a number other than 1 that divides both evenly, divide them both by that number.

Example

Simplify the following fractions.

$\frac{6}{8}$ $\frac{7}{14}$ $\frac{8}{11}$

$\frac{6}{8}$: 6 and 8 have a GCF of 2, so divide both 6 and 8 by 2.

$\frac{6 \div 2}{8 \div 2} = \frac{3}{4}$

$\frac{7}{14}$: 7 and 14 have a GCF of 7, so divide both 7 and 14 by 7.

$\frac{7 \div 7}{14 \div 7} = \frac{1}{2}$

$\frac{8}{11}$: 8 and 11 have a GCF of 1, so the fraction is already simplified.

Practice

Directions: For Numbers 1 through 10, simplify each fraction.

19

Sample code:

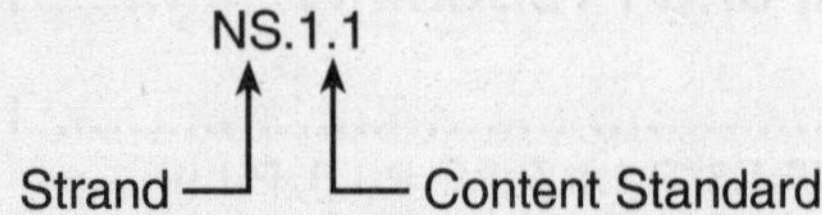

Strands: NS = Number Sense
AF = Algebra and Functions
MG = Measurement and Geometry
P = Statistics, Data Analysis, and Probability

Introduction

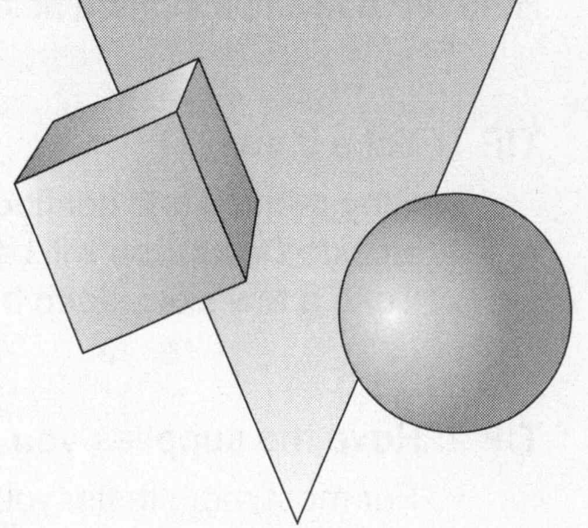

Why do we learn math? For some of us, it's just fun! For others, it can sometimes be a lot of work. But we all need to learn math. Every day, people around the world use math in many different ways.

How much money do I need to buy this milk? How tall should this building be? How can we send a rocket into space? All of these questions are answered using math. You have been learning about math as long as you have been in school, and now you are about to learn more. Someday you will use math to answer many questions—maybe even how to send a rocket into space!

This book will give you lots of practice answering math questions. This workbook also has lots of tips to help you do your best at math. It will help you become a better problem solver. Each lesson will teach you important math skills.

Test-Taking Tips

Here are a few tips that will help you on test day.

TIP 1: Take it easy.

Stay relaxed and confident. Because you've practiced the problems in *Buckle Down*, you will be ready to do your best on almost any math test. Take a few slow, deep breaths before you begin the test.

TIP 2: Have the supplies you need.

For most math tests, you will need two sharp pencils and an eraser. Your teacher will tell you whether you need anything else.

TIP 3: Read the questions more than once.

Every question is different. Some questions are more difficult than others. If you need to, read a question more than once. This will help you make a plan for solving the question.

TIP 4: Learn to "plug in" answers to multiple-choice items.

When do you "plug in"? You should "plug in" whenever your answer is different from all of the answer choices or you can't come up with an answer. Plug each answer choice into the problem and find the one that makes sense. (You can also think of this as "working backwards.")

TIP 5: Check your work.

Take the time to check your work on every problem. By checking your work, you can eliminate careless mistakes.

TIP 6: Use all the test time.

Work on the test until you are told to stop. If you finish early, go back through the test and double-check your answers. You just might increase your score on the test by finding and fixing any errors you might have made.

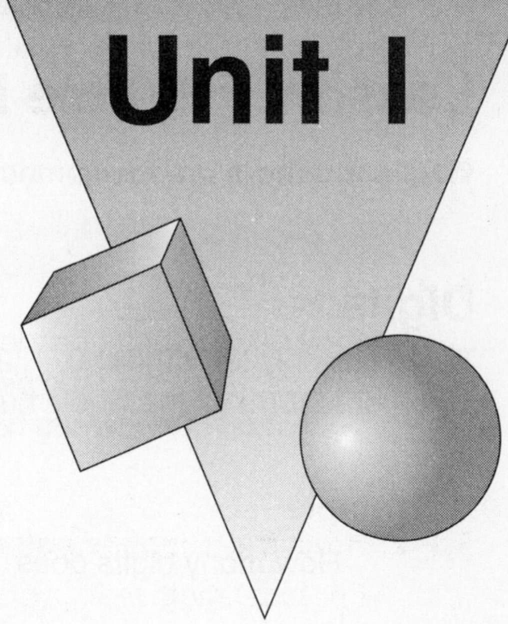

Unit 1

Number Sense

Every number has a name. You know some of them. The name for 1 is "one." But what is the name for 987?

In this unit, you will show, read, and write whole numbers up to 1,000 using digits, drawings, and words. You will order and compare whole numbers. You will add, subtract, multiply, and divide whole numbers. You will write fractions to name a part of a whole object or a part of a set of objects. You will also find the value of a set of coins.

Lesson 1: Whole Numbers

Whole numbers are the numbers you count with: 0, 1, 2, 3, 4, and so on.

Digits

There are only ten **digits:** 0, 1, 2, 3, 4, 5, 6, 7, 8, and 9. These ten digits join together to form all the whole numbers.

Example

How many digits does 138 have?

The number 138 has three digits. The digits are 1, 3, and 8.

Drawings

Whole numbers can be shown with **drawings**. You can use the blocks to show drawings of whole numbers.

Example

This shows **one (1).**

This shows **ten (10).**

This shows **one hundred (100).**

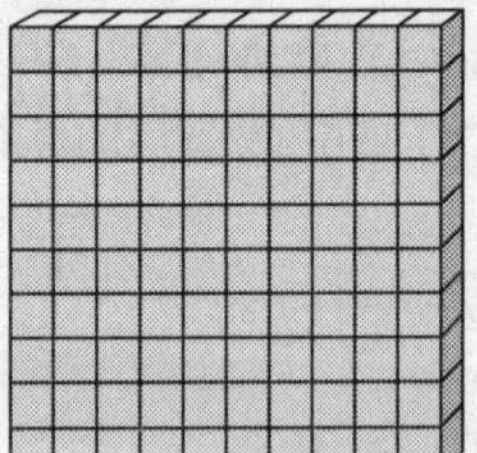

Content Standards: NS.1.1, NS.1.2

Example

How is 138 shown in a drawing?

The following drawing shows 138.

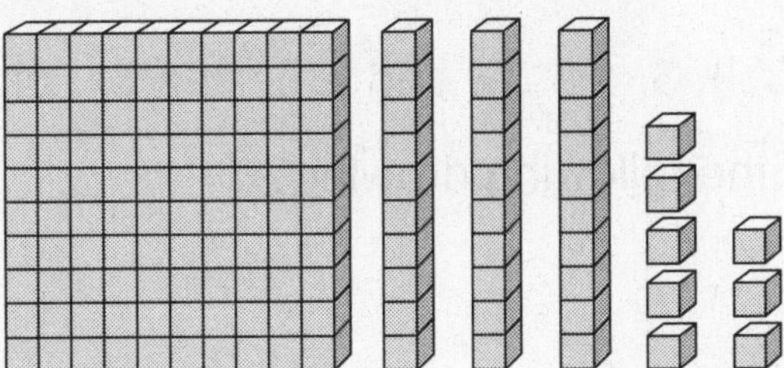

Number drawings also make it easy to see how to write a number in **expanded form**. The number 138 written in expanded form is 100 + 30 + 8. You could also write this number in expanded form like this: 1 hundred + 3 tens + 8 ones.

Words

Numbers have names, just like people. The word for a number is what you would call it out loud. The following table shows the names for ones, tens, and hundreds.

1	one	10	ten	100	one hundred
2	two	20	twenty	200	two hundred
3	three	30	thirty	300	three hundred
4	four	40	forty	400	four hundred
5	five	50	fifty	500	five hundred
6	six	60	sixty	600	six hundred
7	seven	70	seventy	700	seven hundred
8	eight	80	eighty	800	eight hundred
9	nine	90	ninety	900	nine hundred

TIP: If you have ten hundreds, the number is 1,000. The name for this number is "one thousand."

Content Standards: NS.1.1, NS.1.2

Example

What is the word form of 138?

The word form of 138 is one hundred thirty-eight.

Example

What number is shown in the following drawing?

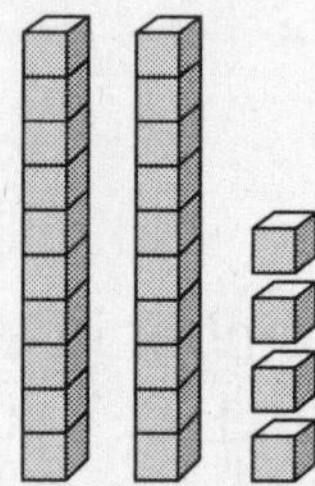

Write the **number:** 24

Write the **expanded form:** 20 + 4 or 2 tens + 4 ones

Write the **word form:** twenty-four

Example

What number is shown in the following drawing?

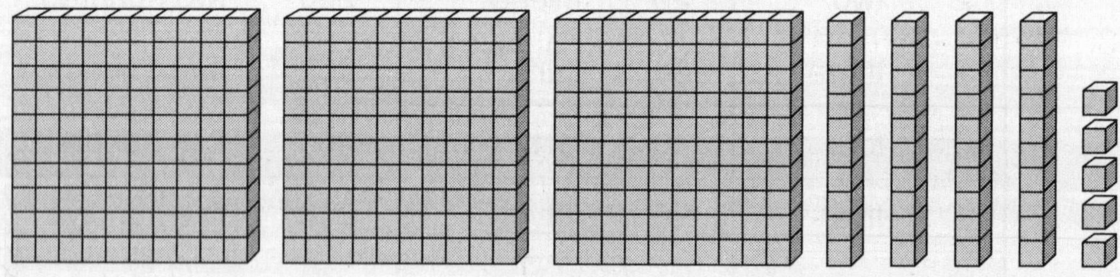

Write the **number:** 345

Write the **expanded form:** 300 + 40 + 5 or
3 hundreds + 4 tens + 5 ones

Write the **word form:** three hundred forty-five

Content Standards: NS.1.1, NS.1.2

Practice

1. How many students are in your classroom?

   Write the number: ______________________

   Write the expanded form: ______________________

   Write the word form: ______________________

2. What number is shown in the following drawing?

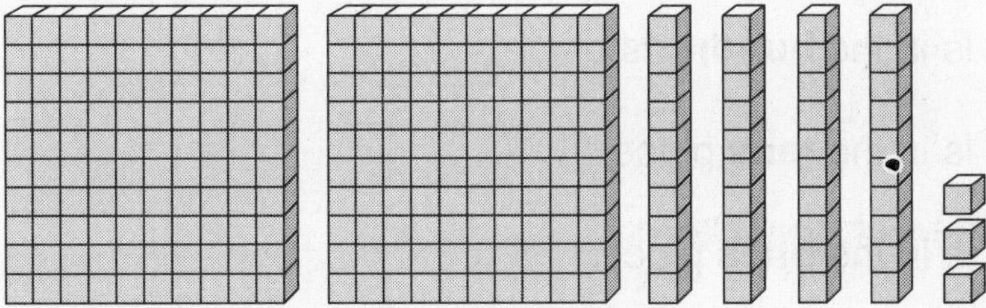

   Write the number: ______________________

   Write the expanded form: ______________________

   Write the word form: ______________________

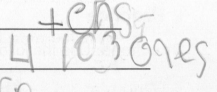

3. What number is shown in the following drawing?

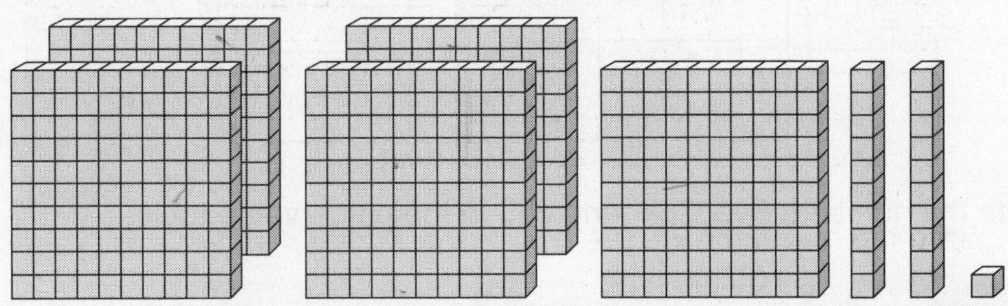

   Write the number: ______________________

   Write the expanded form: ______________________

   Write the word form: ______________________

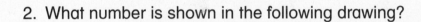

Place Value

Each digit of a number has a **place value**. A digit's place value is where it fits in the number.

Example

The following place-value table shows the place value of each digit of 527.

Hundreds	Tens	Ones
5	2	7

The 5 is in the **hundreds** place.

The 2 is in the **tens** place.

The 7 is in the **ones** place.

Practice

Directions: Use the following place-value table to answer Numbers 1 through 4.

Hundreds	Tens	Ones
8	9	0
7	0	4
6	4	3

1. Write the numbers 890, 704, and 643 in the place-value table.

2. What is the place value of the 8 in 890? ____________

3. What digit is in the ones place in 704? ____________

4. What is the place value of the 4 in 643? ____________

Content Standards: NS.1.3

Ordering Numbers

Numbers have an order: 2 always goes after 1 and before 3. You use this order to count and compare numbers. The following chart shows some of the counting numbers in order from 1 to 100.

1	2	3	4	5	6	7	8	9	10
11	12	13	14	15	16	17	18	19	20
21	22	23	24	25	26	27	28	29	30
31	32	33	34	35	36	37	38	39	40
41	42	43	44	45	46	47	48	49	50
51	52	53	54	55	56	57	58	59	60
61	62	63	64	65	66	67	68	69	70
71	72	73	74	75	76	77	78	79	80
81	82	83	84	85	86	87	88	89	90
91	92	93	94	95	96	97	98	99	100

Now it's your turn to practice! Fill in the rest of the chart above.

You can use the chart on page 9 to help you order numbers.

Examples

What number comes **after** 23?

20, 21, 22, 23, **24**

The number **24** comes **after** 23.

What are the next 3 numbers **after** 39?

39, **40**, **41**, **42**

The next 3 numbers **after** 39 are **40**, **41**, and **42**.

You can also use a number line to help you order numbers.

Examples

What number comes **after** 23?

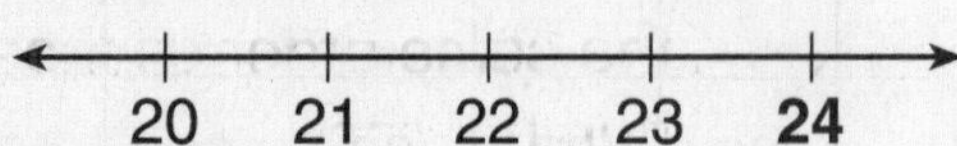

The number **24** comes **after** 23.

What are the next 3 numbers **after** 39?

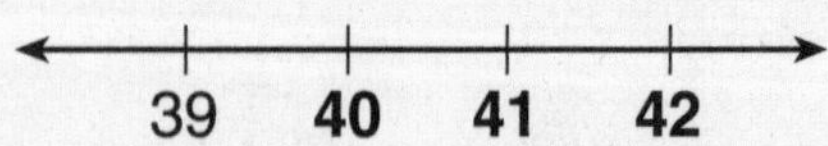

The next 3 numbers **after** 39 are **40**, **41**, and **42**.

Content Standards: NS.1.3

Practice

Directions: For Numbers 1 and 2, write the next three numbers.

1. 92, 93, 94, 95, 96, 97

2. 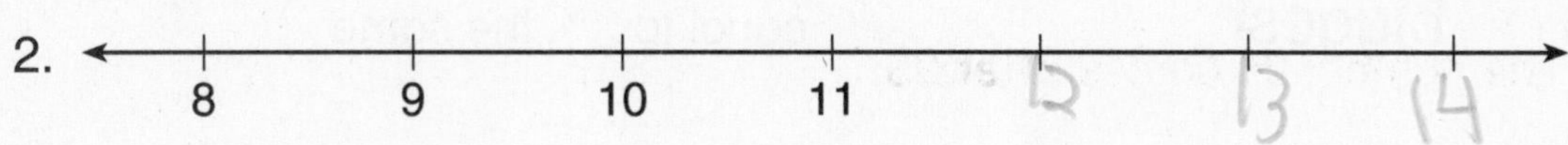

Directions: Use the following number line to answer Numbers 3 through 5.

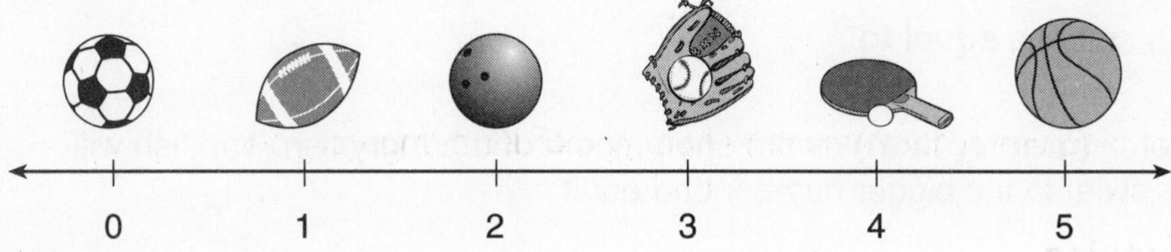

3. Circle the object located at 5.

4. Circle the number where the  is located.

1 2 3

5. Circle the row of objects that is in the same order as those on the number line.

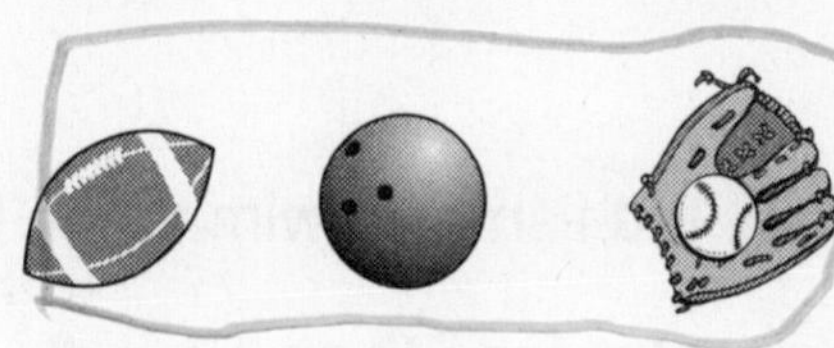

Comparing Numbers

When you compare numbers, you will see words like these:

greater	greatest	smaller	smallest
larger	largest	less	least
bigger	biggest	equal to	the same

You can use the following symbols to compare numbers.

$>$ means **greater than**

$<$ means **less than**

$=$ means **equal to**

Think of $>$ **(greater than)** as the open mouth of a hungry fish. The fish will *always* swim to the bigger number and eat it.

The fish will swim to the bigger number: 10

Since 10 is **greater than** 9, write **10 $>$ 9**.

You can also think of $<$ **(less than)** as the open mouth of a hungry fish.

Again, the fish will swim to the bigger number: 17

Since 12 is **less than** 17, write **12 $<$ 17**.

Content Standards: NS.1.3

You can use a place-value table to help you compare numbers.

Example

Which number is **greater**, 19 or 16?

Tens	Ones
1	9
1	6
↑ same	↑ different

Look at the tens place first. The digits are the same. Look at the ones place next.

The 9 is greater than the 6. The number that has the 9 in the ones place is the greater number.

So, 19 is greater than 16. $19 > 16$

Example

Which number is **greater**, 848 or 828?

Hundreds	Tens	Ones
8	4	8
8	2	8
↑ same	↑ different	↑ same

Look at the hundreds place first. The digits are the same. Look at the tens place next.

The 4 is greater than the 2. The number that has the 4 in the tens place is the greater number.

So, 848 is greater than 828. $848 > 828$

Practice

Directions: For Numbers 1 through 16, compare the numbers. Write the correct symbol on each blank.

>	greater than
<	less than
=	equal to

1. 75 ________ 63
2. 51 ________ 51
3. 49 ________ 72
4. 199 ________ 187
5. 356 ________ 653
6. 710 ________ 810
7. 511 ________ 155
8. 1,000 ________ 1,000
9. 38 ________ 83
10. 46 ________ 45
11. 17 ________ 9
12. 108 ________ 202
13. 634 ________ 634
14. 412 ________ 553
15. 331 ________ 331
16. 906 ________ 843

Content Standards: NS.1.3

Directions: Use the following place-value table to answer Numbers 17 through 19.

Hundreds	Tens	Ones
4	3	2
4	8	2

17. Compare 432 and 482. What place value is different? tens

18. Which number is **greater**: 432 or 482? 482

19. Use symbols to compare the numbers.

432 < 482 482 > 432

Directions: Three people played a game. Each person's score is listed below. Use the list to answer Numbers 20 and 21.

John: 487 points

Renee: 492 points

Saul: 481 points

20. If the winner of the game had the **highest** score, who won the game?

renee

21. If the winner of the game had the **lowest** score, who won the game?

saul

Practice Questions

1

578

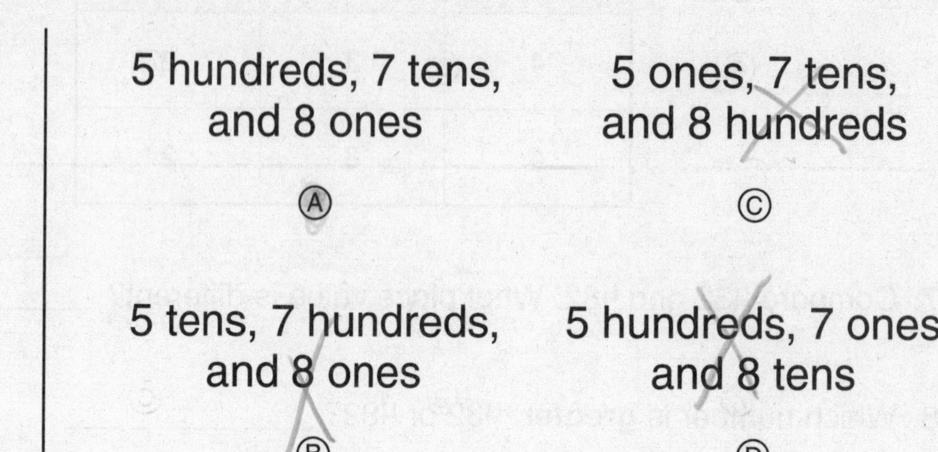

5 hundreds, 7 tens, and 8 ones
Ⓐ
5 ones, 7 tens, and 8 hundreds
Ⓒ
5 tens, 7 hundreds, and 8 ones
Ⓑ
5 hundreds, 7 ones and 8 tens
Ⓓ

2

19, 20, ____, ____, ____

21, 22, 24	21, 23, 25	21, 22, 23	21, 23, 24
Ⓐ	Ⓑ	Ⓒ	Ⓓ

3

$63 < 65$	$16 = 24$	$92 > 92$	$32 < 29$
Ⓐ	Ⓑ	Ⓒ	Ⓓ

4

150 153 513 1503

Ⓐ Ⓑ Ⓒ Ⓓ

5

274 129 532 802

Ⓐ Ⓑ Ⓒ Ⓓ

6

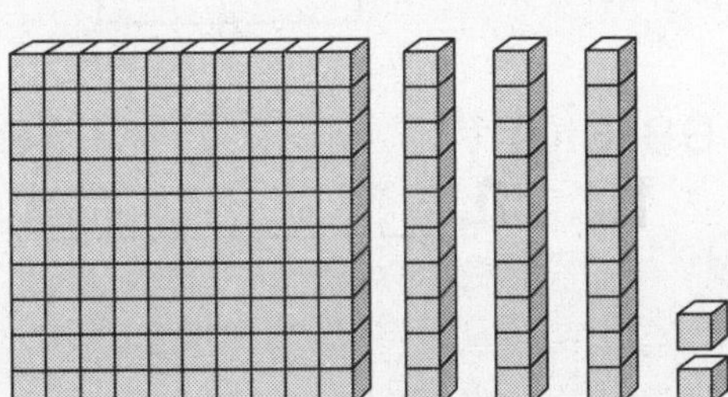

32 123 132 312

Ⓐ Ⓑ Ⓒ Ⓓ

7

107

Ⓐ 10 tens and 7 ones

Ⓑ 1 hundred and 7 tens

Ⓒ 1 ten and 7 ones

Ⓓ 17 tens

8

738

Ⓐ seven three-eight

Ⓑ seventy-three eight

Ⓒ seventy thirty-eight

Ⓓ seven hundred thirty-eight

9

914

Ⓐ 9 + 1 + 4

Ⓑ 9 + 10 + 4

Ⓒ 900 + 10 + 4

Ⓓ 90 + 1 + 4

Content Standards: NS.2.2

Lesson 2: Addition and Subtraction

In this lesson, you will review addition and subtraction. You will also learn about how addition and subtraction are related.

Addition

When you **add**, you combine (put together) two numbers.

Example

How many quarters are there altogether?

2 1

To get the answer, combine the sets of numbers.

3

There are 3 quarters altogether.

You can write an **addition number sentence** for this problem. The numbers you add are called **addends**. These are the **parts**. The answer is called the **sum**. This is the **whole**.

$2 + 1 = 3$ ← **sum**

↑ ↑

addends

Practice

Directions: For Numbers 1 and 2, write the number of objects on each blank under the pictures. Add to find how many objects there are altogether.

1\.

______ + ______ = ______

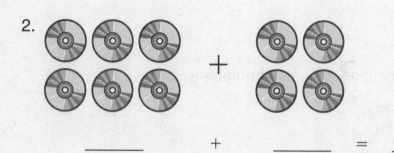

2\.

______ + ______ = ______

Directions: For Numbers 3 through 14, find the sum.

3\. 9 + 7 = ______

4\. 8 + 5 = ______

5\. 7 + 6 = ______

6\. 4 + 3 = ______

7\. 2 + 9 = ______

8\. 9 + 8 = ______

9\. 5 + 4 = ______

10\. 1 + 8 = ______

11\. 6 + 3 = ______

12\. 2 + 1 = ______

13\. 4 + 4 = ______

14\. 1 + 5 = ______

Content Standards: NS.2.2

Adding Two- and Three-Digit Numbers

Sometimes you will need to add larger numbers. One way to add two-digit numbers is to use models.

Example

Add: 45 + 51

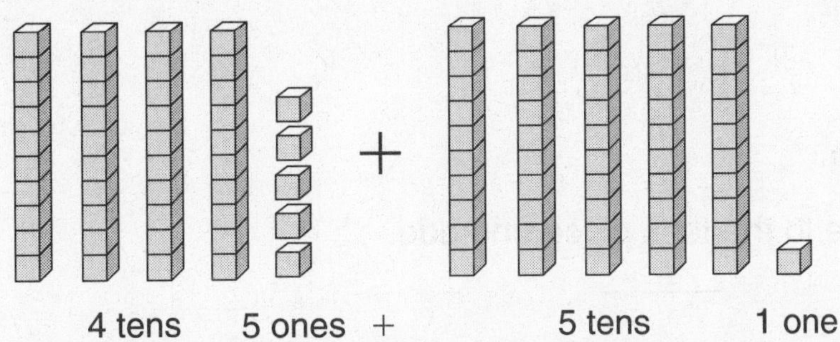

Step 1: **Add the ones.**

5 ones + 1 one = 6 ones

Step 2: **Add the tens.**

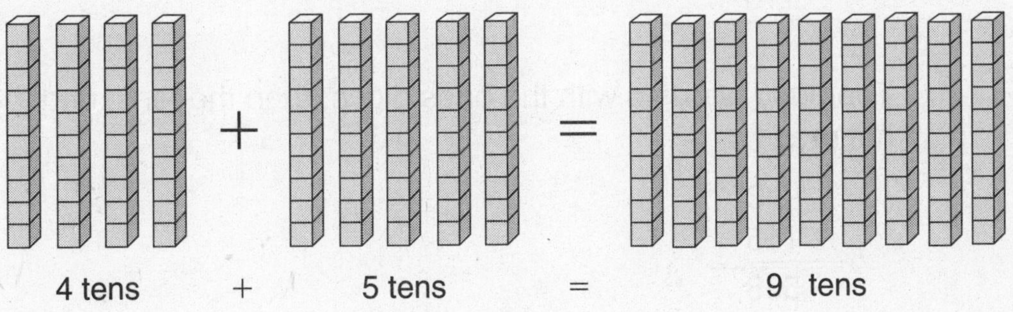

The sum is 96. (There are 96 blocks altogether.)

You can also find the sum without using models. First line up the place values. Then add, starting with the ones place.

Example

Add: 45 + 51

Line up the ones places and the tens places. Then add the ones place.

$$\begin{array}{r} 45 \\ +\ 51 \\ \hline 6 \end{array}$$

Now move to the tens place and add.

$$\begin{array}{r} 45 \\ +\ 51 \\ \hline 96 \end{array}$$

The sum is 96. (45 + 51 = 96)

Example

Add: 443 + 115

Line up the place values.

$$\begin{array}{r} 443 \\ +\ 115 \\ \hline \end{array}$$

Then add, starting with the ones place, then the tens, and then the hundreds.

$$\begin{array}{r} 443 \\ +\ 115 \\ \hline 558 \end{array}$$

The sum is 558. (443 + 115 = 558)

Content Standards: NS.2.2

Practice

Directions: For Numbers 1 through 8, find the sum.

1. 12 + 47 = ________

2. 223 + 162

3. 552 + 127 = ________

4. 71 + 25

5. 531 + 163 = ________

6. 13 + 62

7. 33 + 54 = ________

8. 625 + 233

Adding with Regrouping

Sometimes when you add two- or three-digit numbers, you will need to regroup.

Example

Add: 18 + 23

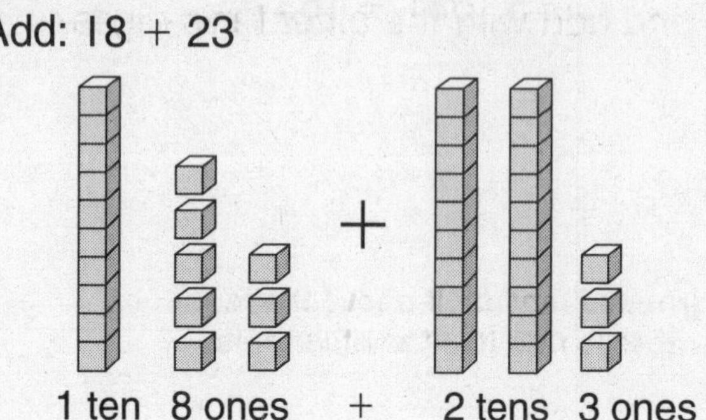

1 ten 8 ones + 2 tens 3 ones

Step 1: **Add the ones.**

8 ones + 3 ones = 11 ones

Step 2: **Regroup the ones when you have more than 9 ones.**

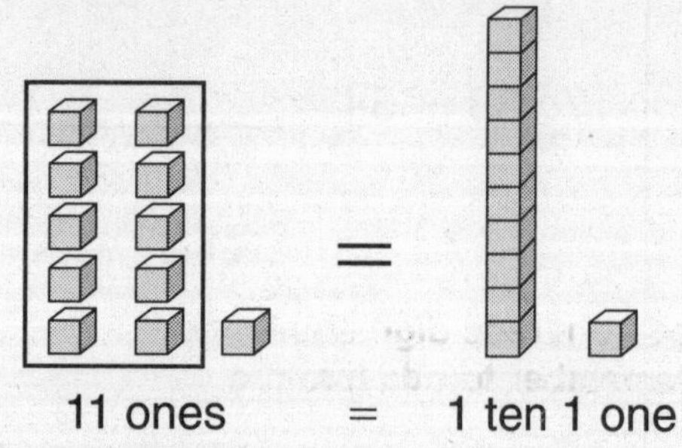

11 ones = 1 ten 1 one

Step 3: **Add the tens.**

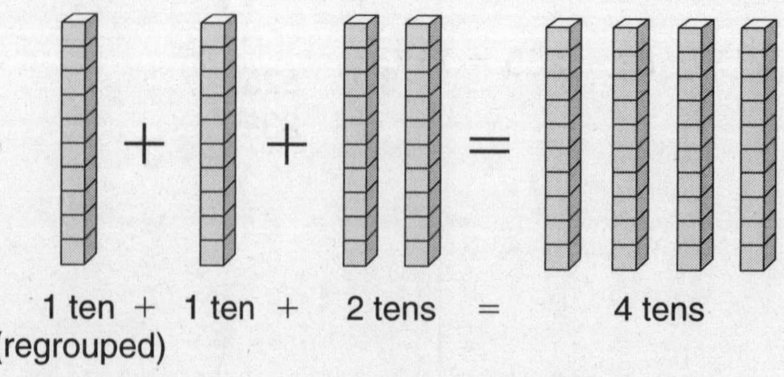

1 ten (regrouped) + 1 ten + 2 tens = 4 tens

The sum is 41. (There are 41 blocks altogether.)

Content Standards: NS.2.2

You can also find the sum without models. This is the way you will add numbers most of the time.

When the numbers in the ones place add up to more than 9, regroup 10 ones as 1 ten. For example, 12 ones becomes 1 ten and 2 ones. Write the ones digit in the sum. Add a 1 to the tens place and add with the other tens digits.

Example

Add: 18 + 23

$$\begin{array}{r} 1 \\ 18 \\ +\ 23 \\ \hline 41 \end{array}$$

Write the regrouped tens digit above the tens place. Remember to add it to the other tens.

The sum is 41. (18 + 23 = 41)

When the numbers in the tens place add up to more than 9, regroup 10 tens as 1 hundred. For example, 15 tens becomes 1 hundred and 5 tens. Write the tens digit in the sum. Add a 1 to the hundreds place and add with the other hundreds digits.

Example

Add: 482 + 235

$$\begin{array}{r} 1 \\ 482 \\ +\ 235 \\ \hline 717 \end{array}$$

Write the regrouped hundreds digit above the hundreds place. Remember to add it to the other hundreds.

The sum is 717. (482 + 235 = 717)

Practice

Directions: For Numbers 1 through 8, find the sum. Remember to regroup if there are more than 9 ones or tens.

1. 284 + 362 = ________

2. $\begin{array}{r} 29 \\ +\ 35 \\ \hline \end{array}$

3. 34 + 16 = ________

4. $\begin{array}{r} 384 \\ +\ 371 \\ \hline \end{array}$

5. 742 + 192 = ________

6. $\begin{array}{r} 68 \\ +\ 24 \\ \hline \end{array}$

7. 54 + 17 = ________

8. $\begin{array}{r} 219 \\ +\ 143 \\ \hline \end{array}$

Content Standards: NS.2.2

Subtraction

When you **subtract**, you take away or compare sets of numbers.

Example

Yuna found 5 leaves. Two of them blew away. How many leaves does Yuna have left?

The picture shows that Yuna had five leaves. Because 2 blew away, 2 have been taken away (crossed out).

5 take away 2 is 3. Yuna has 3 leaves left.

You can write a **subtraction number sentence** for this problem. The number you subtract from is the **whole**. The number you subtract is one **part**. The **difference** is the answer.

whole → $5 - 2 = 3$ ← **difference**

↑ **part**

Example

There are 7 pieces of string. There are 5 balloons. How many more pieces of string are there than balloons?

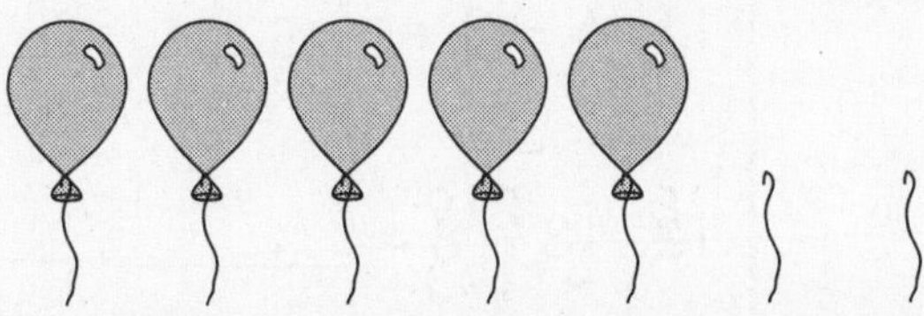

This problem asks you to compare the set of 7 to the set of 5.

There are 2 more pieces of string than balloons.

$7 - 5 = 2$

Practice

1. Paco had 6 fish. He gave 3 away. How many fish does Paco have left? Use the following picture to help find the number of fish Paco has left.

Paco has _____ fish left.

2. Jamie won 9 tickets playing an arcade game. Keisha won 5 tickets. How many fewer tickets did Keisha win than Jamie?

Arcade Ticket	Arcade Ticket	Arcade Ticket	Arcade Ticket	Arcade Ticket	Arcade Ticket	Arcade Ticket	Arcade Ticket	Arcade Ticket

Arcade Ticket	Arcade Ticket	Arcade Ticket	Arcade Ticket	Arcade Ticket

Keisha won _____ fewer tickets than Jamie.

Directions: For Numbers 3 through 14, find the difference.

3. 13 − 7 = _______
4. 8 − 5 = _______
5. 15 − 6 = _______
6. 5 − 4 = _______
7. 14 − 9 = _______
8. 10 − 8 = _______
9. 11 − 3 = _______
10. 9 − 2 = _______
11. 6 − 3 = _______
12. 13 − 8 = _______
13. 12 − 5 = _______
14. 17 − 9 = _______

Content Standards: NS.2.2

Subtracting Two- and Three-Digit Numbers

Sometimes you will need to subtract larger numbers. One way to subtract two-digit numbers is to use models.

Example

Subtract: 24 − 11

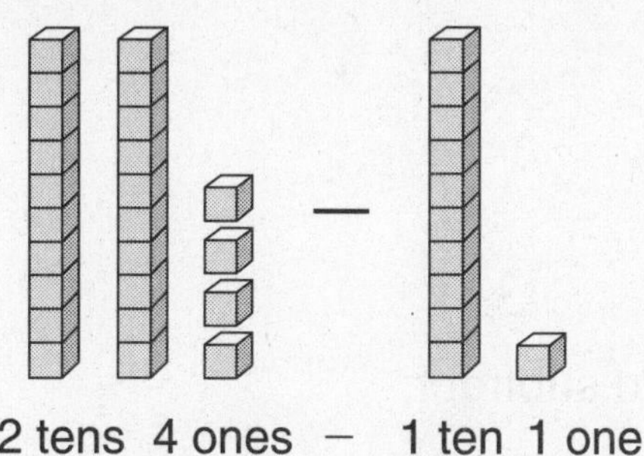

2 tens 4 ones − 1 ten 1 one

Step 1: **Subtract the ones.**

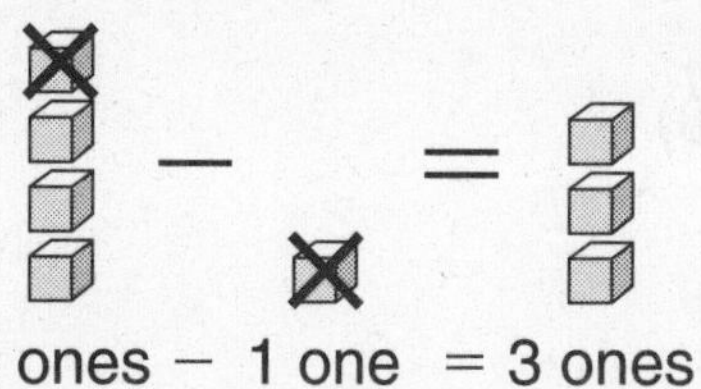

4 ones − 1 one = 3 ones

Step 2: **Subtract the tens.**

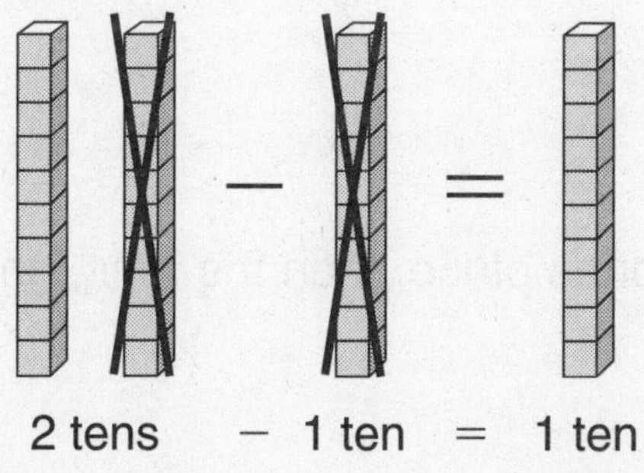

2 tens − 1 ten = 1 ten

When you take 11 away from 24, you get 13. (There are 13 blocks left.)

You can also find the difference without using models. First line up the place values. Then subtract, starting with the ones place.

Example

Subtract: 24 − 11

Line up the ones places and the tens places. Then subtract the ones place.

$$\begin{array}{r} 24 \\ -\ 11 \\ \hline 3 \end{array}$$

Now move to the tens place and subtract.

$$\begin{array}{r} 24 \\ -\ 11 \\ \hline 13 \end{array}$$

The difference is 13. (24 − 11 = 13)

Example

Subtract: 734 − 322

Line up the place values.

$$\begin{array}{r} 734 \\ -\ 322 \\ \hline \end{array}$$

Then subtract, starting with the ones place, then the tens, and then the hundreds.

$$\begin{array}{r} 734 \\ -\ 322 \\ \hline 412 \end{array}$$

The difference is 412. (734 − 322 = 412)

Practice

Directions: For Numbers 1 through 8, find the difference.

1. 46 − 21 = 25

2. 98
   − 72
   26

3. 869 − 625 = 244

4. 742
   − 321
   421

5. 977 − 560 = 417

6. 89
   − 12
   77

7. 564 − 522 = 042

8. 97
   − 35
   62

Subtracting with Regrouping

Sometimes when you subtract two- or three-digit numbers, you need to regroup.

Example

Subtract: 43 − 18

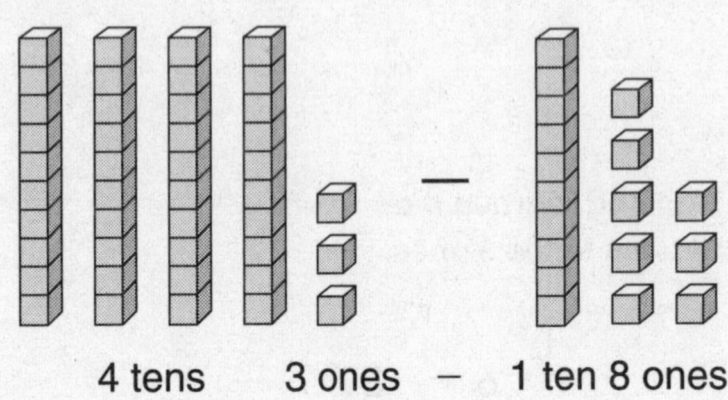

Step 1: **There are not enough ones in the number 43. Borrow a ten and regroup the ones.**

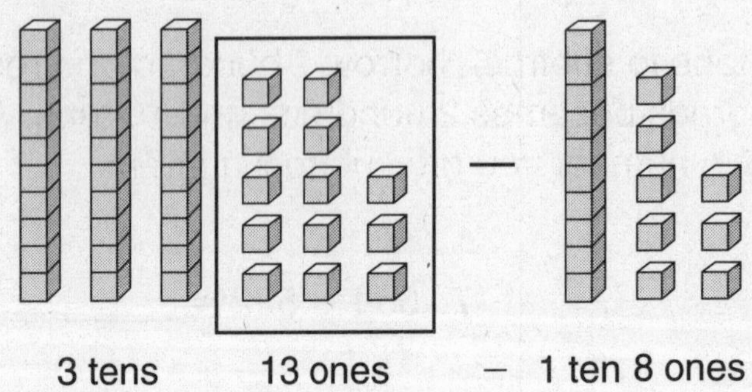

Step 2: **Subtract the ones. Then subtract the tens.**

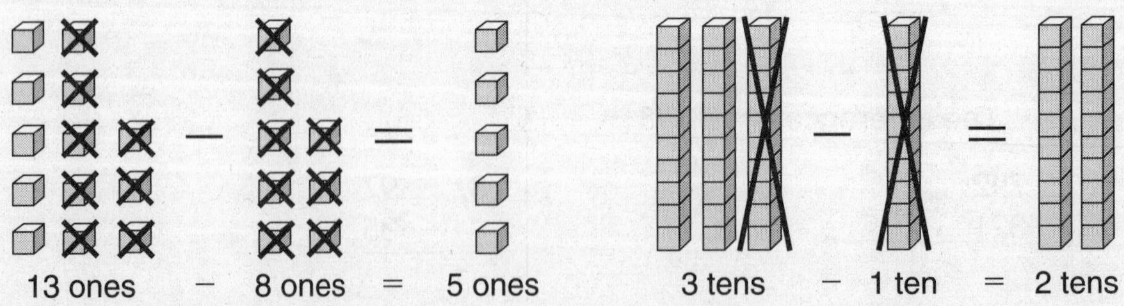

When you take 18 away from 43, you get 25. (There are 25 blocks left.)

Content Standards: NS.2.2

You can also find the difference without using models. This is the way you will subtract numbers most of the time.

When there are not enough ones to subtract, borrow 1 ten and regroup it as 10 ones. For example, 4 tens becomes 3 tens and 10 ones. Add the 10 ones to the ones place in the number you are subtracting from.

Example

Subtract: 43 − 18

```
  3 13 ←—— Borrow a ten and regroup it as 10 ones.
  4̸3̸      Add the 10 ones to the 3 ones.
−  18
 ————
   25
```

The difference is 25. (43 − 18 = 25)

When there are not enough tens to subtract, borrow 1 hundred and regroup it as 10 tens. For example, 3 hundreds becomes 2 hundreds and 10 tens. Add the 10 tens to the tens place in the number you are subtracting from.

Example

Subtract: 314 − 161

```
  2 11 ←—— Borrow a hundred and regroup it as 10 tens.
  3̸1̸4     Add the 10 tens to the 1 ten.
− 161
 ————
  153
```

The difference is 153. (314 − 161 = 153)

Practice

Directions: For Numbers 1 through 8, find the difference. Remember to borrow and regroup where necessary.

1. 428 − 271 = ________

2. 86 − 28

3. 708 − 363 = ________

4. 92 − 35

5. 90 − 19 = ________

6. 982 − 639

7. 85 − 48 = ________

8. 892 − 66

Content Standards: NS.2.1, NS.2.2

Relating Addition to Subtraction

You can use addition to **check** subtraction. Addition and subtraction are **inverse operations**. That means they are opposites, so one can be used to check the other.

Example

There are 8 rectangles below. If you shade 6 of the rectangles, how many rectangles will **not** be shaded?

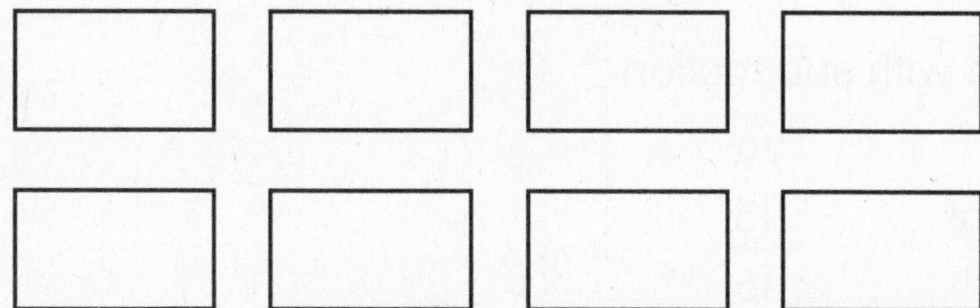

Shade in 6 of the rectangles.

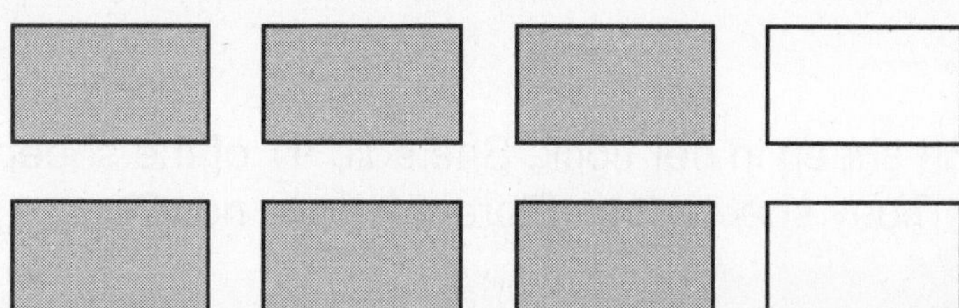

Then, subtract $8 - 6 = 2$. Two of the rectangles are not shaded.

Is the answer correct? Check by adding **6** to **2**.

$6 + 2 = 8$

Because 8 is the number you started with in the subtraction problem above, the subtraction is correct.

$8 - 6 = 2$ and $6 + 2 = 8$ are **related facts**. They are part of a **fact family**. The other facts in the fact family are $8 - 2 = 6$ and $2 + 6 = 8$.

Example

There are 43 boys and 36 girls in the second grade at Tom's school. How many students are in the second grade at Tom's school?

Add 43 + 36.

$$\begin{array}{r} 43 \\ +\ 36 \\ \hline 79 \end{array}$$

Check addition with subtraction.

$$\begin{array}{r} 79 \\ -\ 36 \\ \hline 43 \end{array} \quad \text{or} \quad \begin{array}{r} 79 \\ -\ 43 \\ \hline 36 \end{array}$$

There are 79 students in the second grade at Tom's school.

Example

Florence had 64 sheep in her flock. She sold 41 of the sheep to her neighbor. How many sheep does Florence have now?

Subtract 64 − 41.

$$\begin{array}{r} 64 \\ -\ 41 \\ \hline 23 \end{array}$$

Check subtraction with addition.

$$\begin{array}{r} 23 \\ +\ 41 \\ \hline 64 \end{array} \quad \text{or} \quad \begin{array}{r} 41 \\ +\ 23 \\ \hline 64 \end{array}$$

Florence has 23 sheep remaining.

Content Standards: NS.2.1, NS.2.2

Practice

Directions: For Numbers 1 through 8, find the sum or difference. Then, write a related number sentence to check that the answer is correct.

1. $17 - 9 =$ ______

2. $\begin{array}{r} 8 \\ +\ 6 \\ \hline \end{array}$

3. $93 - 46 =$ ______

4. $\begin{array}{r} 50 \\ +\ 37 \\ \hline \end{array}$

5. $167 - 72 =$ ______

6. $\begin{array}{r} 77 \\ +\ 96 \\ \hline \end{array}$

7. $468 - 332 =$ ______

8. $\begin{array}{r} 314 \\ +\ 563 \\ \hline \end{array}$

Practice Questions

1

$5 + 4 = 9$ Ⓐ

$4 + 4 = 9$ Ⓑ

$5 + 5 = 9$ Ⓒ

$6 + 3 = 9$ Ⓓ

2

$$\begin{array}{r} 5 \\ +\ 9 \\ \hline 14 \end{array}$$

$14 - 9 = 5$ Ⓐ

$5 - 14 = 9$ Ⓑ

$5 + 14 = 19$ Ⓒ

$9 + 14 = 23$ Ⓓ

3

$$\begin{array}{r} 701 \\ -\ 21 \\ \hline \end{array}$$

680 Ⓐ

690 Ⓑ

710 Ⓒ

720 Ⓓ

4

to the ones place Ⓐ

to the hundreds place Ⓒ

to the tens place Ⓑ

You don't have to carry. Ⓓ

5

Humpbacks Seen

Saturday	46
Sunday	43

83 Ⓐ

89 Ⓑ

93 Ⓒ

99 Ⓓ

6

$$\begin{array}{r} 343 \\ +\ 537 \\ \hline \end{array}$$

980 Ⓐ

970 Ⓑ

880 Ⓒ

870 Ⓓ

7

31	39	41	49
Ⓐ	Ⓑ	Ⓒ	Ⓓ

8

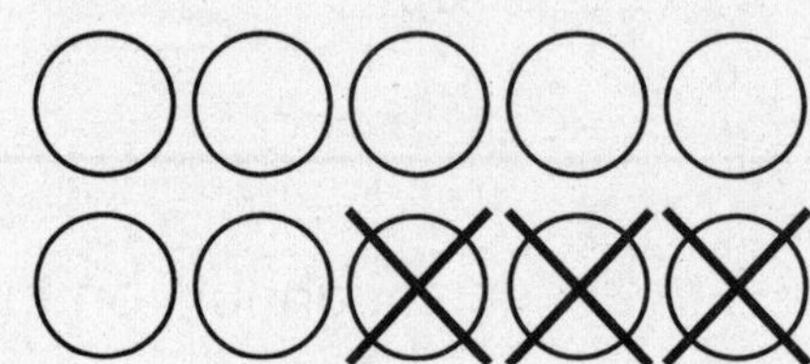

$7 + 3 = 10$ Ⓐ

$10 + 3 = 13$ Ⓑ

$13 - 10 = 3$ Ⓒ

$10 - 3 = 7$ Ⓓ

9

$63 - 45 = 18$

$45 - 18 = 27$ Ⓐ

$63 + 18 = 81$ Ⓑ

$18 + 45 = 63$ Ⓒ

$45 - 63 = 18$ Ⓓ

Content Standards: NS.3.1

Lesson 3: Multiplication and Division

In this lesson, you will review multiplication and division.

Multiplication

When you **multiply**, you add the same amount over and over. Multiplication can be modeled by repeated addition, skip counting, or arranging objects in a rectangular array. The numbers that you multiply are called **factors**. The answer when you multiply is called the **product**.

Example

What is the total number of doughnuts on the following plates?

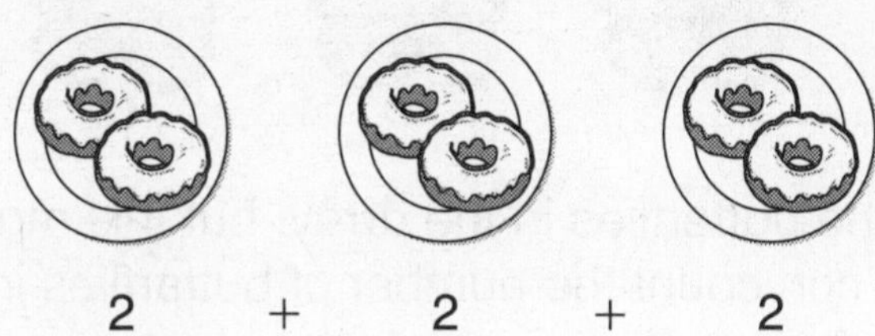

2 + 2 + 2

You can solve this problem using **repeated addition**. Add the number of doughnuts on each plate.

$2 + 2 + 2 = 6$

You can also solve the problem by **skip counting**. Skip count by the number of doughnuts on each plate.

2, 4, 6

There are 2 doughnuts on each plate. There are 3 plates.

You can write this **multiplication number sentence**:

2	×	3	=	6
↑		↑		↑
doughnuts on each plate		**number of plates**		**total number of doughnuts**

There are a total of 6 doughnuts.

You can also use a **rectangular array** to solve a multiplication problem. A rectangular array is a set of objects arranged in the shape of a rectangle.

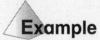

Example

The Discovery Science Center in Orange County has arranged pictures of butterflies in a rectangular array. How many butterflies are shown?

You could count all of the butterflies in the array, but this may take a long time. Instead, you can count the number of butterflies in each row and count the number of rows. Then multiply the numbers.

There are 6 butterflies in each row. There are 3 rows.

6	×	3	=	18
↑		↑		↑
butterflies in each row		**number of rows**		**total number of butterflies**

There are 18 butterfly pictures displayed.

TIP: You can also use repeated addition or skip counting to solve problems arranged in an array. For example:

$6 + 6 + 6 = 18$ 6, 12, 18

Content Standards: NS.3.1

Practice

Directions: Use the following drawing to answer Numbers 1 through 5.

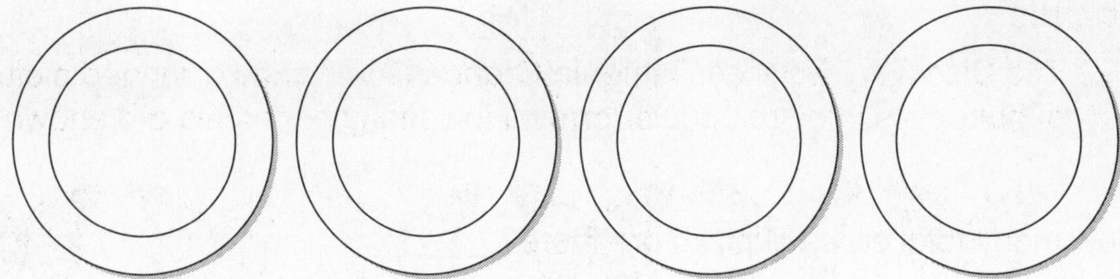

1. Draw 3 cookies on each plate above.

2. How many total cookies are there on the four plates? ________

3. Use repeated addition to show how many cookies there are.

   ________ + ________ + ________ + ________ = ________

4. Use skip counting to show how many cookies there are.

   ________ , ________ , ________ , ________

5. Use multiplication to show how many cookies there are.

   ________ × ________ = ________

6. Look at the following rectangular array of apples. Use repeated addition and multiplication to show how many apples there are.

________ + ________ = ________ and ________ × ________ = ________

Directions: Use the following information to answer Numbers 7 through 9.

The Moores ordered 5 pizzas. Each pizza has 4 equal slices.

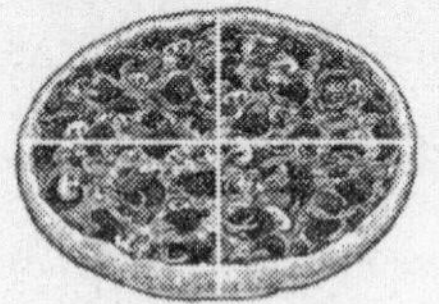 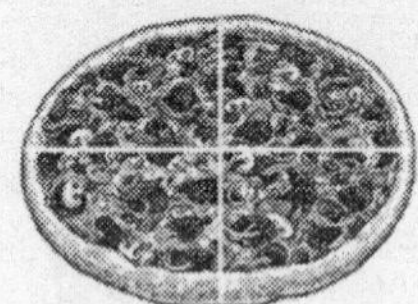 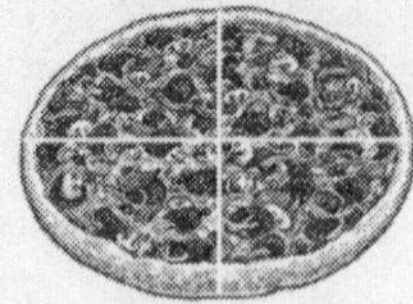 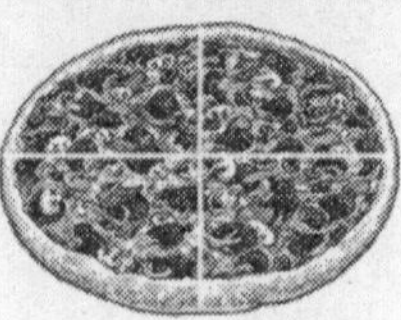 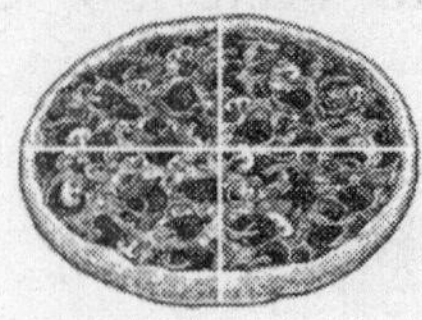

7. How many total slices of pizza are there? ________

8. Use repeated addition to show how many slices there are.

________ + ________ + ________ + ________ + ________ = ________

9. Use multiplication to show how many slices there are.

________ × ________ = ________

Directions: Use the following information to answer Numbers 10 and 11.

The second graders set up chairs so their parents could watch the class play.

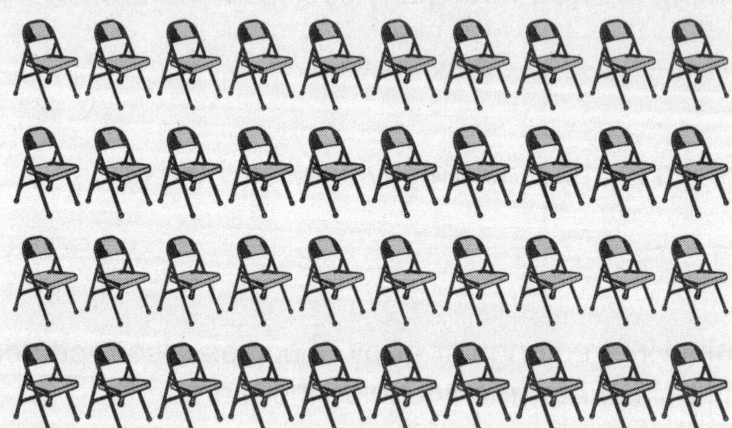

10. Use skip counting to show how many chairs there are.

________ , ________ , ________ , ________

11. Use multiplication to show how many chairs there are.

________ × ________ = ________

Content Standards: NS.3.3

Multiplication Facts

A good way to learn how to do repeated addition, skip counting, or multiplication is to make fact tables.

Practice

Directions: Fill in the following multiplication fact tables. To get you started, some of the spaces have been filled in for you.

1. Multiply by 2s.

×	0	1	2	3	4	5	6	7	8	9	10
2				6						18	

Notice that all the numbers in the table will end in 2, 4, 6, 8, or 0.

2. Multiply by 5s.

×	0	1	2	3	4	5	6	7	8	9	10
5	0						30				

Notice that all the numbers in the table will end in 5 or 0.

3. Multiply by 10s.

×	0	1	2	3	4	5	6	7	8	9	10
10			20						80		

Notice that all the numbers in the table will end in 0.

TIP: These are only a few fact tables. You can also make your own fact tables of other numbers to help you.

Division

When you **divide**, you make smaller, equal groups of objects from a large group. The number you are dividing is called the **dividend**. The number you are dividing by is called the **divisor**. The answer when you divide is called the **quotient**.

When you know the number in each group, division can be modeled by **repeated subtraction**. Start with the total number of objects and subtract the number of objects in each group until you reach 0.

Example

Seth has 12 golden poppies. He put the poppies into groups of 4. How many groups of poppies are there?

You can solve this problem using repeated subtraction. Start with the total number of poppies, 12. Subtract the number of poppies in each group, 4, until you reach 0. Count the number of times you subtracted. This number is the quotient.

$12 - 4 = 8$ (1 time)

$8 - 4 = 4$ (2 times)

$4 - 4 = 0$ (3 times)

You subtracted 4 a total of 3 times.

You can also **form equal groups** to solve this problem. Draw 12 poppies and circle groups of 4.

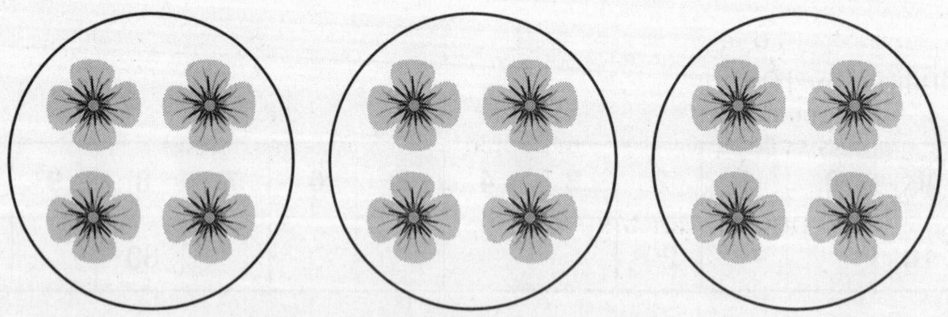

You can write this **division number sentence**:

$$12 \div 4 = 3$$

12	÷	4	=	3
↑		↑		↑
number of poppies		**poppies in each group**		**number of groups**

There are 3 groups of poppies.

Content Standards: NS.3.2

When you know the number of groups, division can be modeled by **sharing equally**.

Example

Sam, Aba, and Becky made 18 sailboats to float on the pond. They shared the sailboats equally among the three of them. How many sailboats did each person get?

Label one sailboat with Sam's name, one with Aba's name, and one with Becky's name. Then start again. Continue until all sailboats are labeled.

There are 6 sailboats labeled with each person's name.

You can write this **division number sentence**:

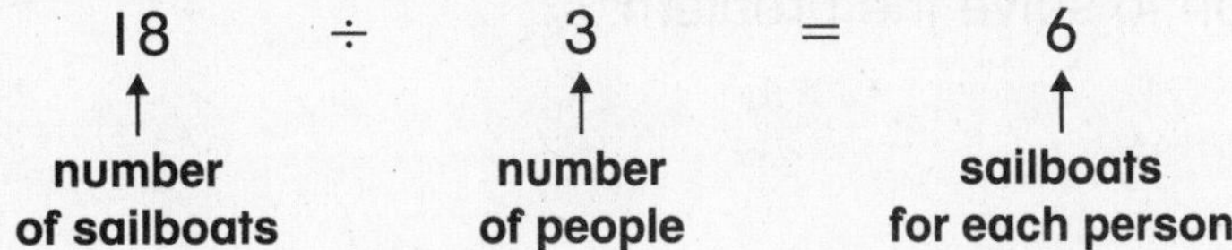

18	÷	3	=	6
↑		↑		↑
number of sailboats		**number of people**		**sailboats for each person**

Each person got 6 sailboats.

Practice

Directions: Use the following information to answer Numbers 1 and 2.

Mrs. Jackson has 24 students in her class. She divided the students into groups of 6.

1. How many groups of students are there? Draw a picture and form equal groups to solve the problem.

   There are __________ groups of students.

2. Use division to show how many groups of students there are.

   _______ ÷ _______ = _______

Directions: Use the following information to answer Numbers 3 and 4.

Gia is at Disneyland. She only has 45 minutes left before the park closes. She needs 15 minutes to get to each ride and complete it.

3. How many rides does Gia have time to go on before the park closes? Use repeated subtraction to solve the problem.

   Gia has time to go on _______ rides before the park closes.

4. Use division to show how many rides Gia has time to go on before the park closes.

   _______ ÷ _______ = _______

Content Standards: NS.3.2

Directions: Use the following information to answer Numbers 5 and 6.

LeBron has 21 sunflower seeds that he wants to plant. He wants to plant them in 7 equal rows.

5. How many sunflower seeds will LeBron plant in each row? Write the row number (1, 2, 3, 4, 5, 6, 7) under each sunflower seed.

LeBron will plant __________ sunflower seeds in each row.

6. Use division to show how many sunflower seeds LeBron will plant in each row.

_______ ÷ _______ = _______

Division with Remainders

Sometimes when you divide there are numbers or objects left over. These numbers or objects are called **remainders (R)**.

Example

Divide these 9 pennies into equal groups of 2. How many groups of 2 are there?

There are 4 groups of 2 and 1 left over.

The one penny that is left over is the remainder (R).

You write this **division number sentence**: 9 ÷ 2 = 4 R1

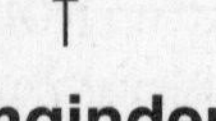

remainder

Example

Dorothy has 20 pieces of chalk. She wants to put all the pieces into boxes. A box will hold 6 pieces of chalk. How many boxes does Dorothy need? Use repeated subtraction.

20 − 6 = 14 (1 time)

14 − 6 = 8 (2 times)

8 − 6 = 2 (3 times with 2 left over)

You subtracted 6 a total of 3 times. There are 2 left over.

3 boxes are full. There are 2 pieces of chalk left over. Dorothy needs 1 more box for the 2 pieces that are left over.

Dorothy needs 4 boxes.

You write this **division number sentence**: 20 ÷ 6 = 3 R2

Content Standards: NS.3.2

Practice

1. Divide these seashells into equal groups of 4.

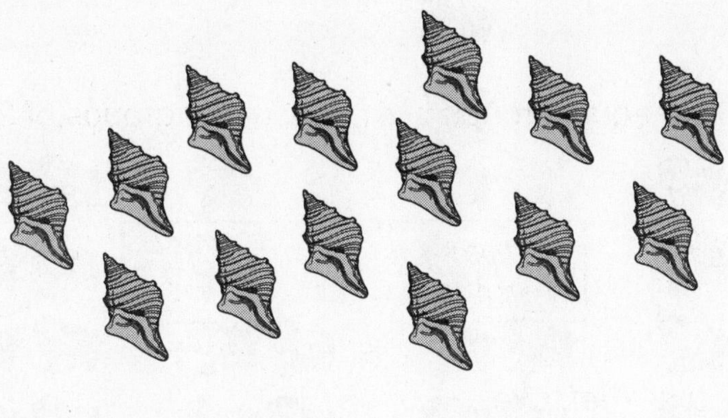

14 ÷ 4 = _____ R _____

2. Ms. Howell has 23 students in her class. She puts all of them that she can into equal groups of 5 students. How many equal groups of 5 students are there? How many students are left over? Use repeated subtraction to solve the problem.

23 ÷ 5 = _____ R _____

There are _____ equal groups of 5 students.

There are _____ students left over.

3. John has 18 apples. He wants to put them into bags. Each bag can hold 7 apples. How many bags does John need?

_____

Show how you found the answer in the space below.

Practice Questions

1

4×2

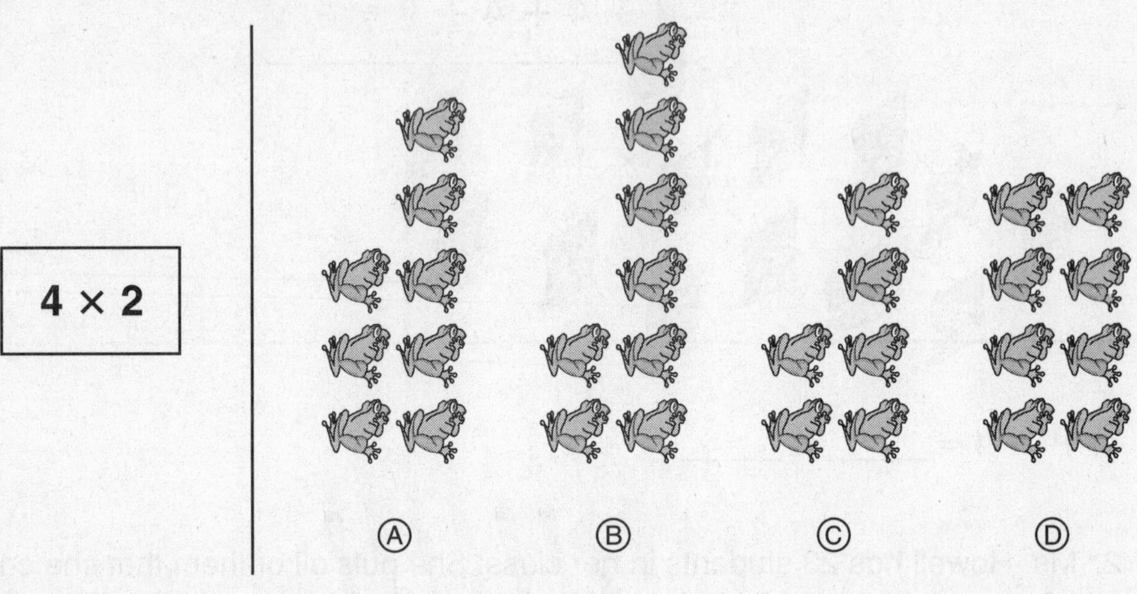

Ⓐ Ⓑ Ⓒ Ⓓ

2

6×10

Ⓐ	Ⓑ	Ⓒ	Ⓓ
6	16	60	66

3

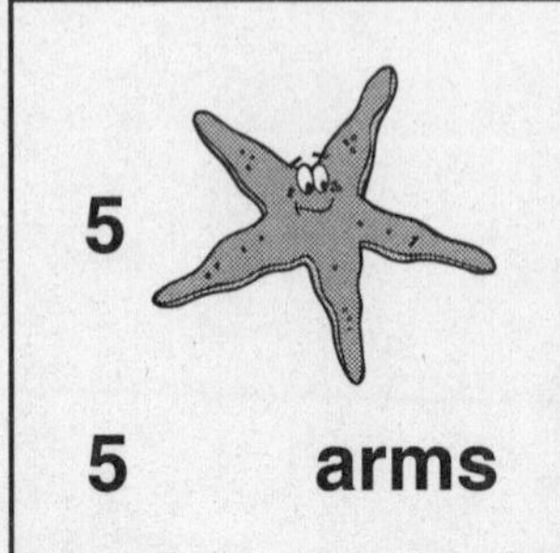

Ⓐ $5 + 5 = 10$

Ⓑ $5 \times 5 = 25$

Ⓒ $5 \times 6 = 30$

Ⓓ $25 \div 5 = 5$

4

4 + 4 + 4 + 4 + 4

4×5	4×4	5×5	5×8
Ⓐ	Ⓑ	Ⓒ	Ⓓ

5

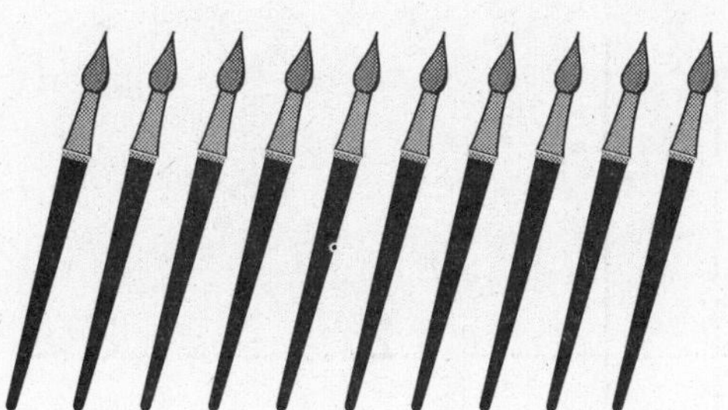

3	3 with 2 left over
Ⓐ	Ⓒ
3 with 1 left over	4
Ⓑ	Ⓓ

6

5 × 7

30	35	40	45
Ⓐ	Ⓑ	Ⓒ	Ⓓ

7

2	3	4	6
Ⓐ	Ⓑ	Ⓒ	Ⓓ

8

7 ÷ 3

2	2 R1	2 R2	3
Ⓐ	Ⓑ	Ⓒ	Ⓓ

Content Standards: NS.4.2

Lesson 4: Fractions

Fractions are numbers between whole numbers. They name parts of a whole. The **numerator (top number)** of the fraction tells how many parts of the whole are special in some way. The **denominator (bottom number)** tells the number of parts the whole is divided into.

numerator → 2
denominator → 5

Words

The word form of a fraction is the same as how you say the fraction out loud. It is the number in the numerator followed by the word for the denominator. The following table shows the words for denominators of 2 through 12.

Denominator	Word Name
2	half (halves)
3	third(s)
4	fourth(s)
5	fifth(s)
6	sixth(s)
7	seventh(s)
8	eighth(s)
9	ninth(s)
10	tenth(s)
11	eleventh(s)
12	twelfth(s)

TIP: The **D**enominator is **D**ownstairs.

Example

What are the word forms of $\frac{1}{2}$, $\frac{3}{4}$, $\frac{5}{9}$, and $\frac{9}{10}$?

$\frac{1}{2}$: one half

$\frac{3}{4}$: three fourths

$\frac{5}{9}$: five ninths

$\frac{9}{10}$: nine tenths

Practice

Directions: For Numbers 1 through 8, write the word form of the given fraction.

1. $\frac{3}{12}$ ____________________

2. $\frac{7}{8}$ ____________________

3. $\frac{1}{5}$ ____________________

4. $\frac{4}{6}$ ____________________

5. $\frac{8}{11}$ ____________________

6. $\frac{7}{7}$ ____________________

7. $\frac{2}{3}$ ____________________

8. $\frac{1}{10}$ ____________________

Content Standards: NS.4.2, NS.4.3

Parts of a Whole

A whole object can be divided into a number of equal parts. To be a fraction, the parts all have to be the same size. A fraction names the part of the whole object that is special in some way.

What fraction of the rectangle is shaded?

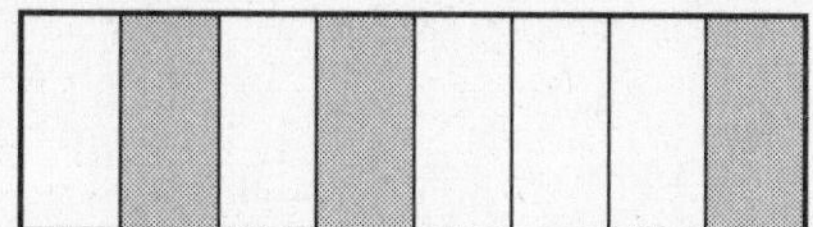

numerator → 3 (parts that are shaded)
denominator → 8 (parts the whole is divided into)

Three eighths, or $\frac{3}{8}$, of the rectangle is shaded.

Fractions can have the same numerator and denominator. When this happens, it means that all of the parts of the whole are special in some way. So, a fraction like this is the same as 1 whole.

What fraction of the rectangle is shaded?

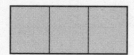

numerator → 3 (parts that are shaded)
denominator → 3 (parts the whole is divided into)

Three thirds, or $\frac{3}{3}$, of the rectangle is shaded. Or, **1 whole** rectangle is shaded.

Practice

1. What fraction of the following circle is shaded? __________

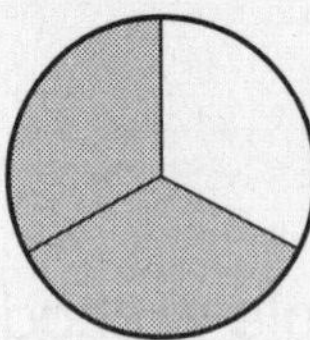

2. Shade three fourths of the following circle.

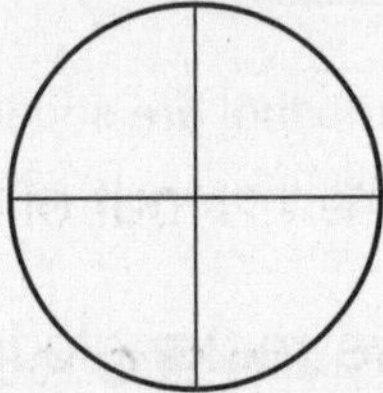

3. Shade $\frac{2}{6}$ of the following rectangle.

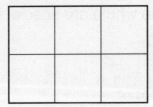

4. What fraction of the following rectangle is shaded? __________

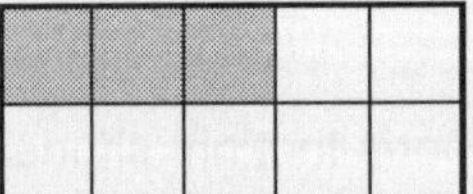

5. Which of the following is the same as 1 whole?

   A. $\frac{1}{10}$

   B. $\frac{8}{9}$

   C. $\frac{4}{4}$

   D. $\frac{2}{1}$

Content Standards: NS.4.2, NS.4.3

Parts of a Set

In this lesson, you learned that a fraction can name a part of a whole, like one half of a slice of pizza. A fraction can also name a part of a set, like one out of a set of two lions.

Example

Set of 2
Here is a set of 2 lions.

There is 1 lion that is shaded. **1** out of **2** lions is shaded.

One half, or $\frac{1}{2}$, of the lions are shaded.

Example

Set of 3
Here is a set of 3 lions.

There are 2 lions that are shaded. **2** out of **3** lions are shaded.

Two thirds, or $\frac{2}{3}$, of the lions are shaded.

Example

Set of 4
Here is a set of 4 lions.

There are 4 lions that are shaded. **4** out of **4** lions are shaded.

Four fourths, or $\frac{4}{4}$, of the lions are shaded. Or, the **whole** set of lions is shaded.

Content Standards: NS.4.2, NS.4.3

Practice

Directions: Use the following picture to answer Numbers 1 and 2.

1. What fraction of the fruit are apples? ________

2. What fraction of the fruit are bananas? ________

Directions: For Numbers 3 through 7, write the fraction that names the shaded part of the set.

3.  ________

4.  ________

5. 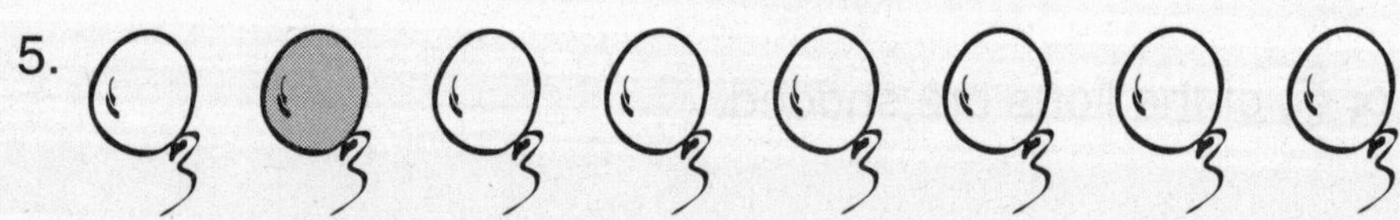 ________

6.  ________

7.  ________

Content Standards: NS.4.1

Unit Fractions

A **unit fraction** has a 1 in the numerator. You can use same-sized circles or other drawings to show and compare unit fractions. When you compare unit fractions, the fraction with the larger denominator is the smaller fraction.

Example

Compare the fractions that show the shaded parts of the following circles.

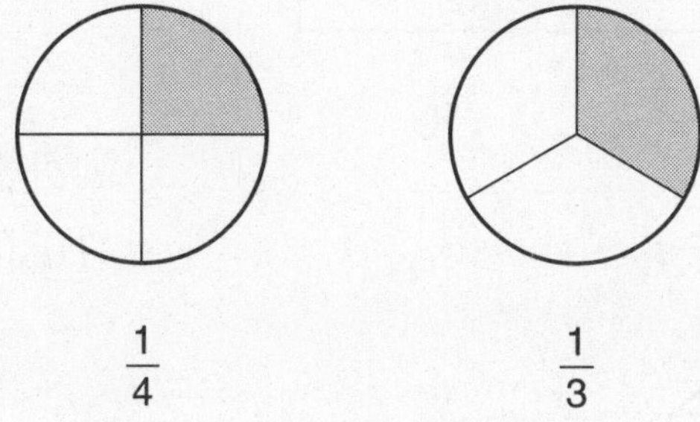

The whole circles are the same size. The shaded part of the first circle is less than the shaded part of the second circle.

$\frac{1}{4} < \frac{1}{3}$

Example

Compare the fractions that show the striped parts of the following sets of marbles.

Both sets have marbles that are the same size. There is 1 striped marble out of 6 in the first set and 1 striped marble out of 10 in the second set.

$\frac{1}{6} > \frac{1}{10}$

Practice

Directions: For Numbers 1 through 4, write the fraction that shows the shaded part underneath each object. Then compare the two fractions by writing <, >, or = in the blank between the objects.

1. 

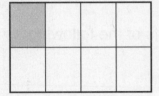

   ________ ______ ________

2. 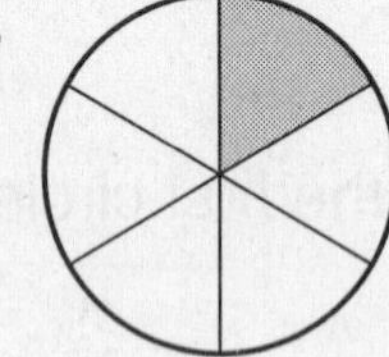 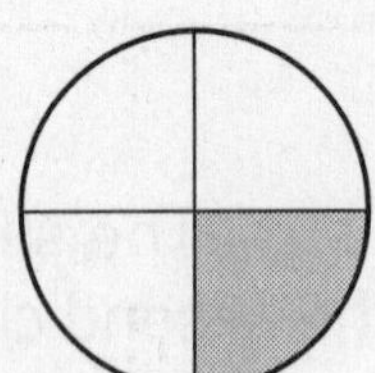

   ________ ______ ________

3. 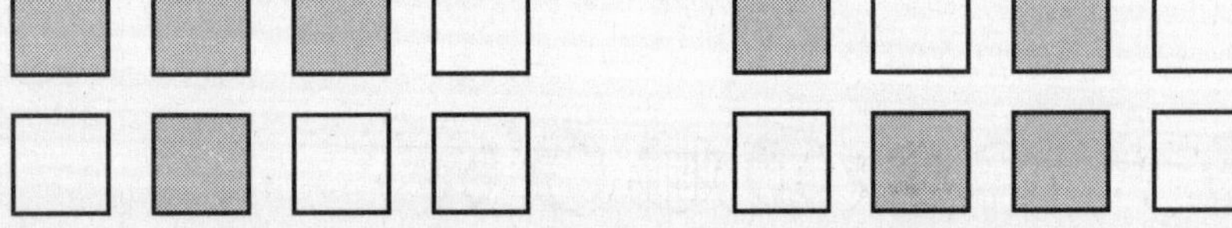

   ________ ______ ________

4. 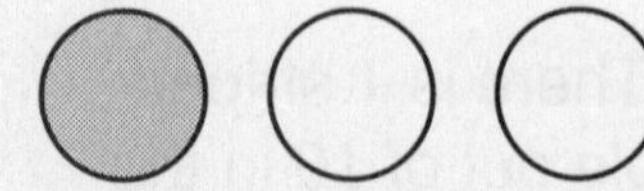  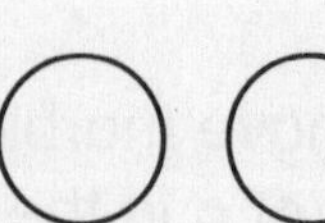 

   ________ ______ ________

Practice Questions

1

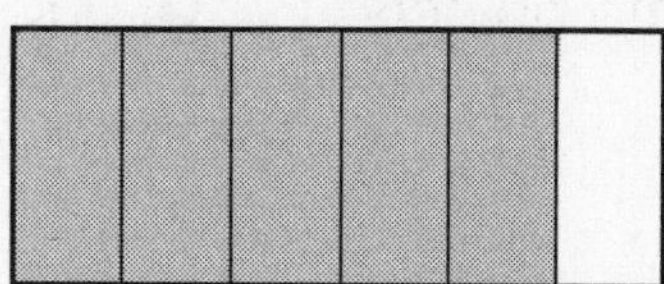

Ⓐ $\frac{5}{1}$ Ⓑ $\frac{5}{6}$ Ⓒ $\frac{1}{5}$ Ⓓ $\frac{1}{6}$

2

Ⓐ $\frac{2}{4}$ Ⓑ $\frac{2}{6}$ Ⓒ $\frac{3}{6}$ Ⓓ $\frac{4}{2}$

3

Ⓐ $\frac{1}{10}$ Ⓑ $\frac{1}{9}$ Ⓒ $\frac{10}{10}$ Ⓓ $\frac{10}{1}$

4

$\frac{2}{9}$

Ⓐ Ⓑ Ⓒ Ⓓ

5

$\frac{4}{4}$

one half Ⓐ

one whole Ⓑ

four wholes Ⓒ

four ones Ⓓ

6

Ⓐ

Ⓑ

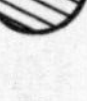

Ⓒ

Ⓓ

7

Ⓐ $\frac{1}{9}$ Ⓑ $\frac{1}{6}$ Ⓒ $\frac{1}{12}$ Ⓓ $\frac{1}{3}$

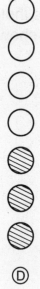

Lesson 5: Money

Knowing the value of **money** is important in everyday life. Shown below are the coins that are most often used, along with their values. A one-dollar ($1) bill is also shown.

= 1¢

penny

= 5¢ = (5 pennies)

nickel

= 10¢ = (2 nickels)

dime

= 25¢ = (2 dimes and 1 nickel)

quarter

= 100¢

one dollar
$1.00

Content Standards: NS.5.1, NS.5.2

Writing Money

Money amounts can be written in word form or using symbols. The symbols that can be used to write money amounts are a **cent sign (¢)** or a **dollar sign ($)**. When using the dollar sign, a **decimal point (.)** separates the dollars from the cents. There are 100 cents in a dollar (100¢ = $1). Each cent is 0.01 of a dollar. Each 10 cents is 0.10 of a dollar.

The following table shows some money amounts written in word form and using symbols.

Word Form	Symbols
seven cents	7¢ or $0.07
twenty-three cents	23¢ or $0.23
one dollar and forty-one cents	141¢ or $1.41

Counting Money

To count a collection of coins, start with the coins of greatest value. Then continue with coins of lesser value.

What is the total value of the following amount of money?

Start with the quarters, then the dimes, then the nickel, and finally the pennies. Add the amounts as you go from left to right.

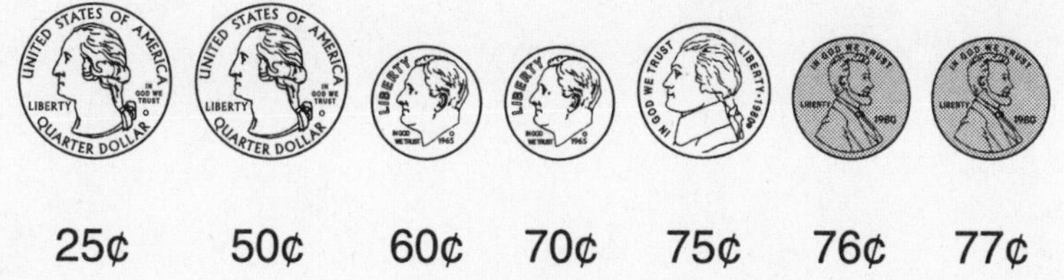

25¢ 50¢ 60¢ 70¢ 75¢ 76¢ 77¢

The total value is seventy-seven cents, 77¢, or $0.77.

To count a collection of bills and coins, first count the bills. Then count the coins.

Example

What is the total value of the following amount of money?

First count the bills. Then count the coins starting with the quarter, then the dimes, and finally the nickel.

$1.00

$2.00

$2.25

$2.35

$2.45

$2.50

The total value is two dollars and fifty cents or $2.50.

Content Standards: NS.5.1, NS.5.2

Practice

Directions: For Numbers 1 through 4, count the total value of the amount of money shown. Write the amount using symbols.

1.          ______

2.          ______

3.       ______

4.      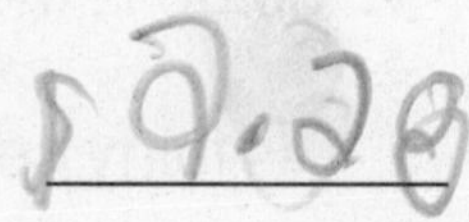 ______

5. Circle the coins to show 83¢. (There is more than one way to show this amount.)

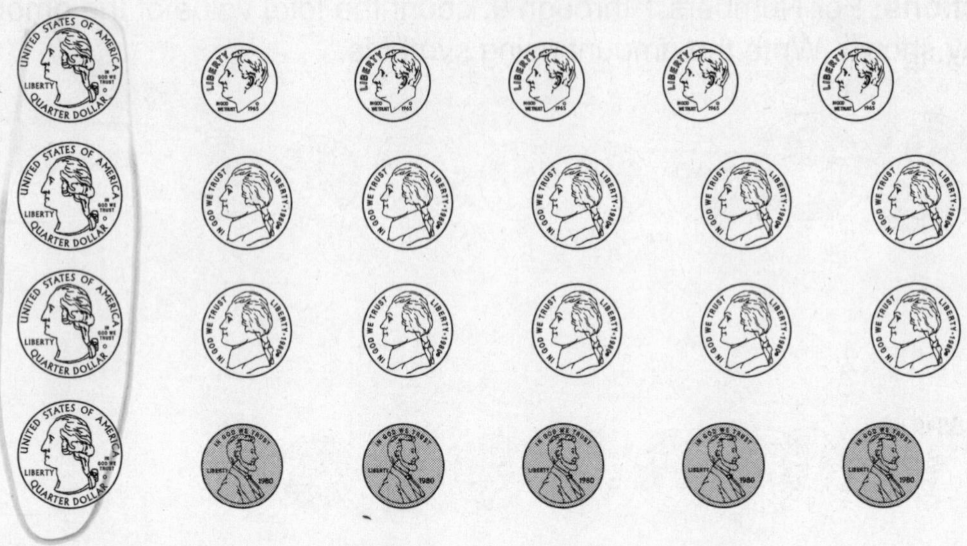

Directions: For Numbers 6 through 10, circle the correct answer.

6. Twenty cents is the same as:

   $20 $0.20

7. Three dollars and ten cents is the same as:

   $310 $3.10

8. Six cents is the same as:

   $0.06 $0.60

9. $0.03 is the same as:

   thirty cents   three cents

10. $1.08 is the same as:

    one dollar and eighty cents   one dollar and eight cents

Content Standards: NS.5.1, NS.5.2

Directions: For Numbers 11 through 15, use the sets of coins shown for each person.

Paula 

Francis 

Cynthia 

Yeng 

11. Which person has the **most** money? ______________________

12. Which person has the **least** money? ______________________

13. Which person has $0.61? ______________________

14. Which person has $0.66? ______________________

15. Which person has $0.58? ______________________

Practice Questions

1

thirty-nine cents
Ⓐ

forty-nine cents
Ⓒ

forty-four cents
Ⓑ

seventy-nine cents
Ⓓ

2

$1.95 Ⓐ

$2.05 Ⓑ

$2.45 Ⓒ

$2.55 Ⓓ

3

= 84¢

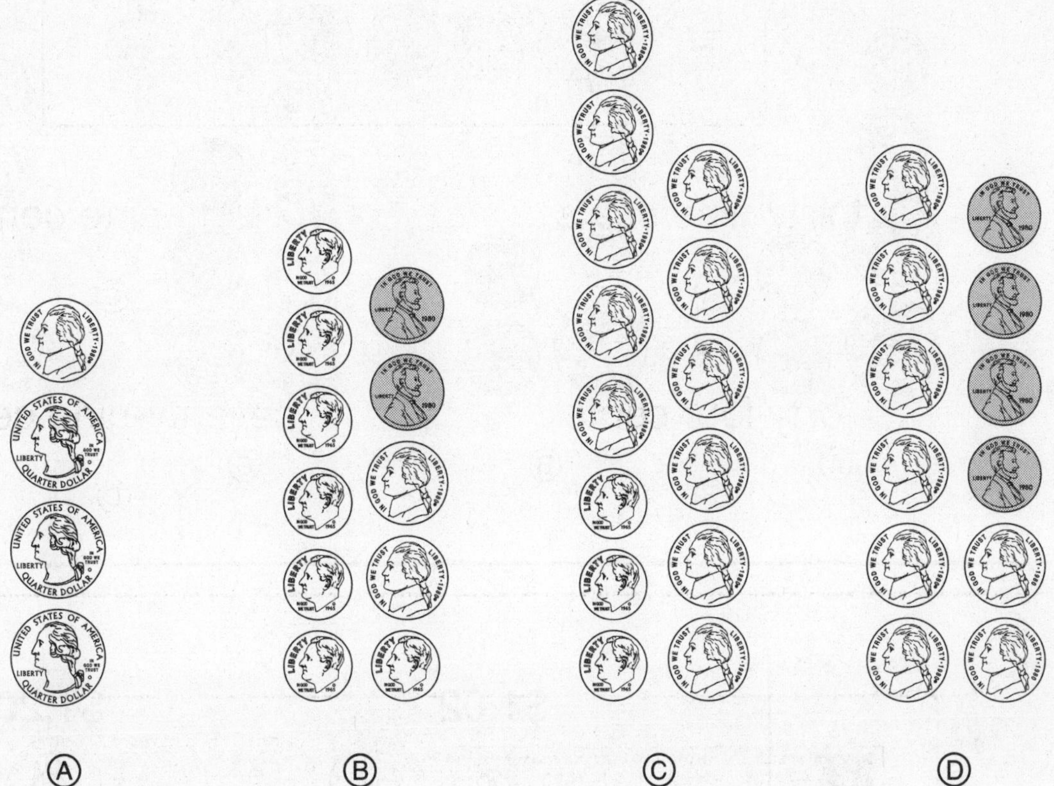

Ⓐ Ⓑ Ⓒ Ⓓ

4

63¢	58¢	53¢	48¢
Ⓐ	Ⓑ	Ⓒ	Ⓓ

5

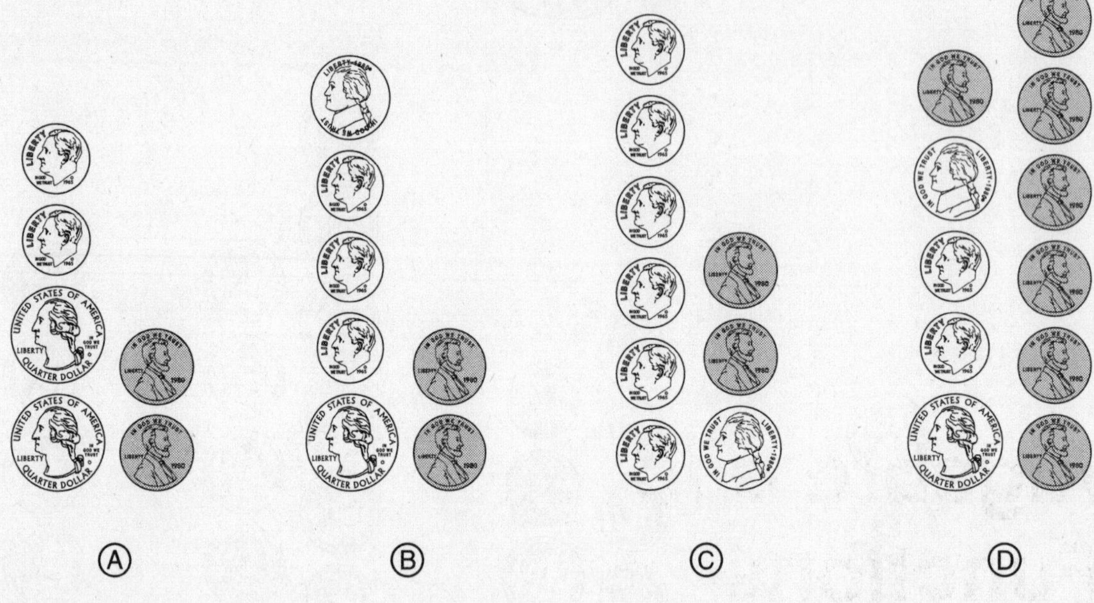

Ⓐ Ⓑ Ⓒ Ⓓ

6

12¢	
$1.02 Ⓐ	$1.20 Ⓒ
$0.12 Ⓑ	$0.21 Ⓓ

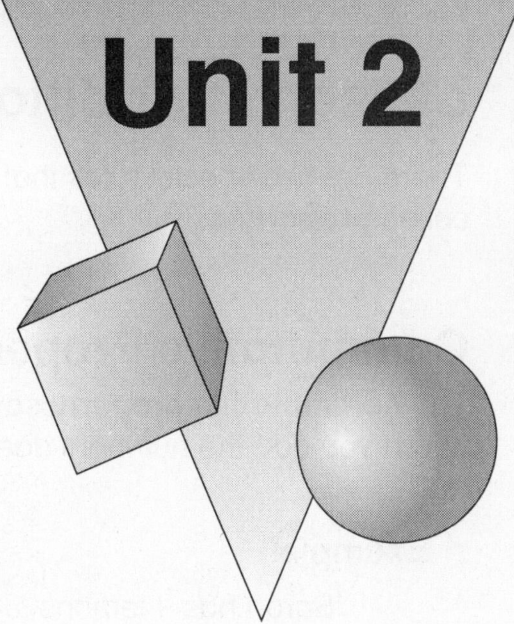

Algebra and Functions

Numbers are like your friends. If Sam comes over, and then Chris, you have fun. If Chris comes over, and then Sam, you have fun. Sam and Chris, Chris and Sam. However you say it, you still have fun.

In this unit, you will change the order and grouping of numbers in addition problems. You will see that this does not change your answer. You will also use what you know about addition and subtraction to help you solve problems.

In This Unit

Lesson 6: Addition Rules

There are two special rules that are true when you add numbers. These rules are called **properties**.

Commutative Property

The **commutative property** says that when you add two numbers, the order in which you add the numbers does not matter.

Example

Sarah has 4 lemons. Jason has 3 lemons. How many lemons do Sarah and Jason have together?

4 + 3 = 7

There are 7 lemons altogether.

Now, add the lemons in a different order, with Jason's lemons first.

3 + 4 = 7

There are still 7 lemons altogether.

When adding two numbers, the order of the two numbers does not matter. The sum will be the same either way.

TIP: You can always check your addition in any problem by switching the order and adding again. The sums should be the same.

Content Standards: AF.1.1

Practice

1. In Lesson 1, you learned how to write numbers using blocks. Draw blocks to show 8 + 6. Do not draw the answer.

2. Draw blocks to show 6 + 8. Do not draw the answer.

3. How many total blocks did you draw in Number 1? ____________

4. How many total blocks did you draw in Number 2? ____________

Directions: For Numbers 5 through 8, fill in the missing numbers.

5. 48 + 76 = 124, so 76 + 48 = __________

6. 23 + 45 = 68, so __________ + 23 = 68

7. 15 + 16 = 31, so 16 + 15 = __________

8. 42 + 68 = 110, so 68 + __________ = 110

Associative Property

The **associative property** says that when you add three numbers, it does not matter which two you group together to add first.

Example

What is the sum?

3 + 4 + 5

Add 3 and 4 together first. This is shown using **parentheses ( )**. Then add 5 to that sum.

(3 + 4) + 5

7 + 5

12

The sum is 12.

Now try adding again. This time add 4 and 5 together first. Then add 3 to that sum.

3 + (4 + 5)

3 + 9

12

The sum is 12.

When adding three numbers, it does not matter which two numbers you add together first. The sum is always the same.

TIP: You can always check the addition of three numbers by grouping two other numbers first and adding again.

Content Standards: AF.1.1

Practice

1. Add the three numbers using grouping. Add 4 and 9 first.

   (4 + 9) + 8

2. Add the three numbers using grouping another way. Add 9 and 8 first.

   4 + (9 + 8)

3. Are the sums in Numbers 1 and 2 the same? ______________

4. Add the three numbers using grouping. Show your work.

   23 + 12 + 8

5. Add the three numbers using grouping. Show your work.

   14 + 6 + 15

Using Both Rules

Sometimes you can use the two rules you just learned to do mental math.

Example

What is the sum?

18 + 17 + 12

Look carefully at the numbers. The 18 and the 12 would be better to add first because they make a nice round sum: 30. It is easier to add numbers that end in zero to other numbers. Switch the order of the numbers so that the 18 and the 12 are next to each other.

18 + 12 + 17

Add the 18 and the 12 first. Then add the 17.

(18 + 12) + 17

30 + 17

47

The sum is 47.

You might also have switched the order of the 18 and the 17.

17 + (18 + 12)

17 + 30

47

Notice that the sum is the same.

Content Standards: AF.1.1

Practice

Directions: For Numbers 1 through 3, add the three numbers. Use the two addition rules to help you.

1. 35 + 43 + 25

2. 18 + 34 + 22

3. 30 + 89 + 40

4. Larry added 61, 17, and 9 and got a sum of 97.

   Is his sum correct? Explain your answer.

   ____

   ____

   ____

5. 84 + 58 + 46 = 188. What is 58 + 46 + 84?

   A. 168

   B. 178

   C. 188

   D. 198

Practice Questions

1

$85 + 17 = 102$ $17 + 85 = ?$	210	201	120	102
	Ⓐ	Ⓑ	Ⓒ	Ⓓ

2

$25 + 5 + 32$	30	37	62	72
	Ⓐ	Ⓑ	Ⓒ	Ⓓ

3

$13 + 28 = \square + 13$

13	15	28	41
Ⓐ	Ⓑ	Ⓒ	Ⓓ

4

$4 + 8$

$8 - 4$	$8 + 4$	$4 - 8$	4×8
Ⓐ	Ⓑ	Ⓒ	Ⓓ

Content Standards: AF.1.2, AF.1.3

Lesson 7: Number Sentences

In this lesson, you will learn about writing number sentences to help you solve problems.

Finding a Missing Part

A **number sentence** is just a math problem with an answer, like 2 + 4 = 6. Most of the time you have to find the answer in a number sentence, but there are also times that you have to figure out a missing part.

Example

Katie had 2 beads. She bought some more beads at the store. Now she has 5 beads. How many more beads did Katie buy?

+ ? =

You can write the following number sentence to solve this problem.

2 + _______ = 5

You can find the missing part by counting on to the number of beads Katie had before she went to the store. Count on until you get to the number of beads she now has.

3, 4, 5

This means she bought 3 beads. This is the missing part.

+ =

2 + 3 = 5

Katie bought 3 more beads at the store.

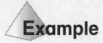

Example

Jacob had 6 mints. He gave some away and now he has 2. How many mints did Jacob give away?

You can write the following number sentence to solve this problem.

6 – ________ = 2

Start with the six mints that Jacob had. Cross out the mints until only 2 are left.

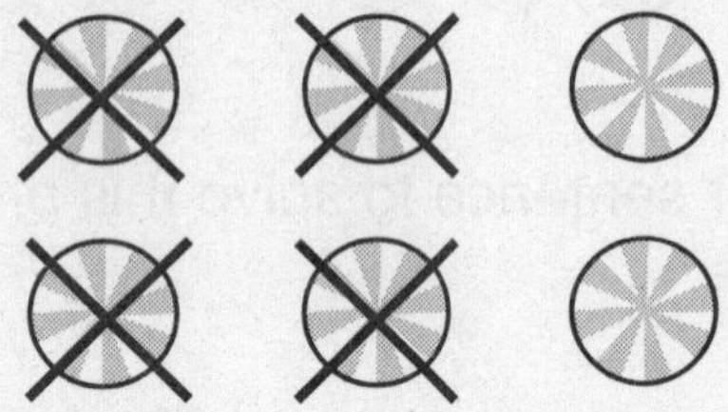

This means that Jacob gave away 4 mints, leaving 2. The missing part is 4. The completed number sentence is 6 – 4 = 2.

Practice

Directions: For Numbers 1 through 4, use the pictures to find the missing part.

1. Amy had 7 bracelets, but she lost some. Now she has 2 bracelets left. How many bracelets did Amy lose?

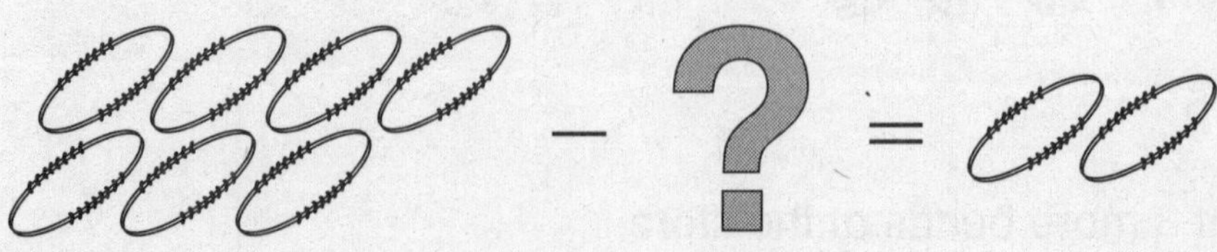

Amy lost ________ bracelets.

Content Standards: AF.1.2, AF.1.3

2. Ling saw 4 dolphins on Saturday and some more on Sunday. She saw 7 dolphins altogether. How many dolphins did Ling see on Sunday?

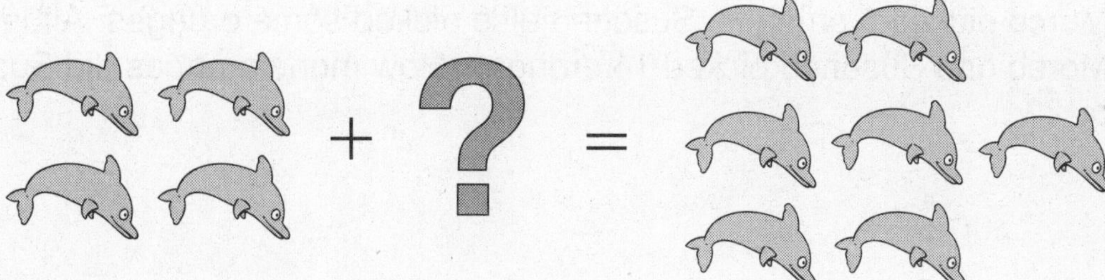

Ling saw ________ dolphins on Sunday.

3. John's team scored 5 runs in the first inning of the kickball game. By the end of the game, his team had 12 runs. How many runs did John's team score after the first inning?

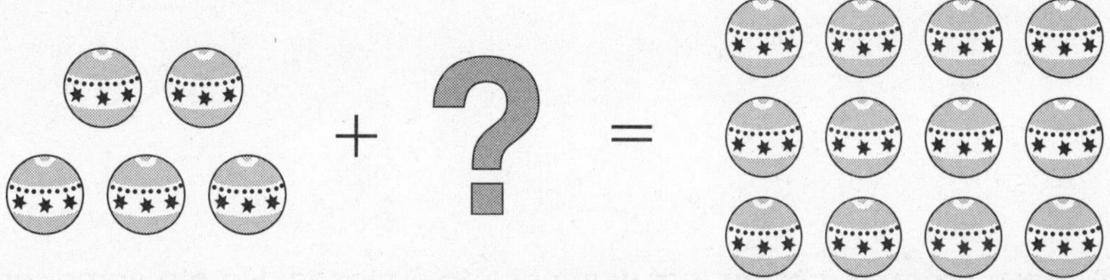

John's team scored ________ runs after the first inning.

4. Drew must eat 8 beans with his dinner. He has 3 beans left to eat. How many beans did Drew already eat?

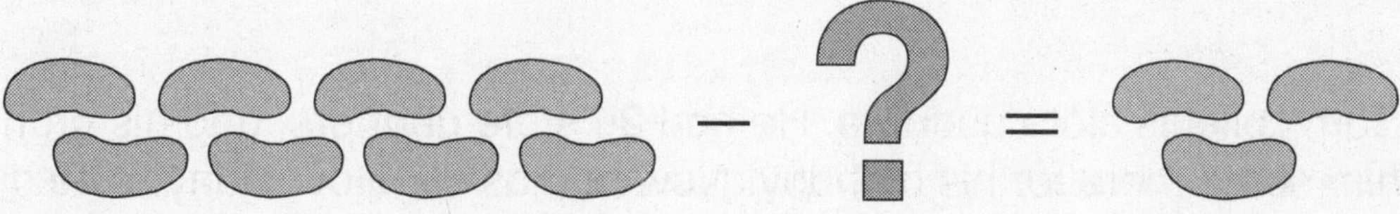

Drew already ate ________ beans.

Directions: For Numbers 5 through 8, write a number sentence to help you find the missing part.

5. Marco picked 5 oranges. Susanna also picked some oranges. Altogether, Marco and Susanna picked 16 oranges. How many oranges did Susanna pick?

6. Bree had $20 in her purse when she went to the mall. She spent some of her money on a new book. Now she has $8 left in her purse. How much did the book cost?

7. Alfonse ordered a pizza that was cut into 8 pieces. He ate some, and now there are 5 pieces left. How many pieces did Alfonse eat?

8. Sam collects state quarters. He had 24 state quarters, and his grandma gave him some more for his birthday. Now he has 29. How many state quarters did Sam's grandma give him?

Content Standards: AF.1.2, AF.1.3

Solving Story Problems

Use the following steps to help you solve story problems.

Step 1: **Understand the problem.**

Don't give up after reading a problem only once! Sometimes a problem will make more sense when you read it a few times. Then you will find out what the problem is asking you to do. It may help to tell yourself the problem in your own words or to draw a picture that shows the problem.

Step 2: **Find what you need.**

Most problems you work with will have numbers. You will need the numbers to solve those problems.

Step 3: **Make a plan.**

If you work with numbers, choose an operation: **addition (+)** or **subtraction (−)**. Write the problem you will solve.

Step 4: **Solve the problem.**

Do the math with the correct operation.

Step 5: **Check your answer.**

You learned in Lesson 2 that addition and subtraction are opposites. Use addition to check a subtraction problem, and use subtraction to check an addition problem.

Step 6: **Write a sentence that gives the answer.**

A story problem often needs words in the answer.

Example

Hannah paid $26 to go to a UCLA Bruins softball camp. She paid $12 for a camp T-shirt. How much money did Hannah pay altogether to go to camp and get a T-shirt?

Step 1: **Understand the problem.**

You need to find the amount of money Hannah spent altogether.

Step 2: **Find what you need.**

This story problem has numbers. Here's what you need:

$26 (cost of the softball camp)

$12 (cost of the camp T-shirt)

Step 3: **Make a plan.**

Most of the time, the word **altogether** means you need to use **addition**. Write the addition problem.

$$\begin{array}{r} 26 \\ +\ 12 \\ \hline \end{array}$$

Step 4: **Solve the problem.**

$$\begin{array}{r} 26 \\ +\ 12 \\ \hline 38 \end{array}$$

Step 5: **Check your answer.**

Use subtraction to check your addition.

$$\begin{array}{r} 38 \\ -\ 26 \\ \hline 12 \end{array}$$

Your answer is correct.

Step 6: **Write a sentence that gives the answer.**

Hannah paid $38 to go to softball camp and buy a T-shirt.

Content Standards: AF.1.2, AF.1.3

Practice

Directions: For Numbers 1 through 6, fill in the blanks to solve the following problem.

The Golden Bears scored a total of 84 points in a basketball game. They scored 45 points before halftime. How many points did the Golden Bears score after halftime?

1. **Understand the problem.**

   What do you need to find?

   ____

2. **Find what you need.**

   Total points scored: ________ Points scored before halftime: ________

3. **Make a plan.**

   Will you need to add or subtract to find the answer? ____________________

4. **Solve the problem.**

5. **Check your answer.**

   Is your answer correct? ________

6. **Write a sentence that gives the answer.**

   ____

Directions: For Numbers 7 through 12, set up a number sentence and solve it. Then write a sentence that gives the answer. Be sure to check your answers.

7. Ramón has 24 seashells. His sister René has 47 seashells. How many seashells do Ramón and René have altogether?

8. Samantha counted 92 birds while hiking in Auburn State Recreation Area. Brady counted 67 birds. How many more birds did Samantha count than Brady?

9. There are 58 counties in the state of California. Of those counties, 16 begin with a letter between A and K. How many counties in California begin with a letter between L and Z?

Content Standards: AF.1.2, AF.1.3

10. At lunch today, there were 87 second graders and 48 third graders in the cafeteria. How many second- and third-grade students were in the cafeteria altogether?

11. Tenielle bought 2 new movies at the video store. One cost $19 and the other cost $15. How much did Tenielle spend on the movies?

12. Martin's bag of chocolate candies had 55 pieces in it. He ate 38 of them. How many chocolate candies are left?

Practice Questions

1

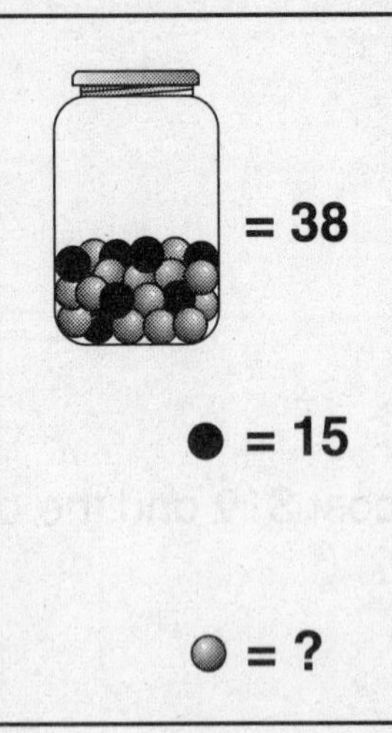

23 white marbles Ⓐ

33 white marbles Ⓑ

43 white marbles Ⓒ

53 white marbles Ⓓ

2

19 Ⓐ

21 Ⓑ

29 Ⓒ

77 Ⓓ

3

___ – 35 = 49

14 Ⓐ

34 Ⓑ

74 Ⓒ

84 Ⓓ

4

$3 + 9 = \_\_\_$ Ⓐ

$9 + \_\_\_ = 3$ Ⓑ

$3 + \_\_\_ = 9$ Ⓒ

$3 - \_\_\_ = 9$ Ⓓ

5

$35 + 15 =$ Ⓐ

$35 - 15 =$ Ⓑ

$15 - 35 =$ Ⓒ

$35 \div 15 =$ Ⓓ

6

Miles from Sacramento

City	Number of Miles
Bishop	273
Paradise	87

186 Ⓐ   196 Ⓑ   214 Ⓒ   361 Ⓓ

7

$8 + \_\_\_ = 12$

4 Ⓐ

6 Ⓑ

8 Ⓒ

20 Ⓓ

8

$23 + \_\_\_ = 4$ Ⓐ

$23 - \_\_\_ = 4$ Ⓒ

$4 - \_\_\_ = 23$ Ⓑ

$23 + 4 = \_\_\_$ Ⓓ

9

104 Ⓐ

312 Ⓒ

116 Ⓑ

322 Ⓓ

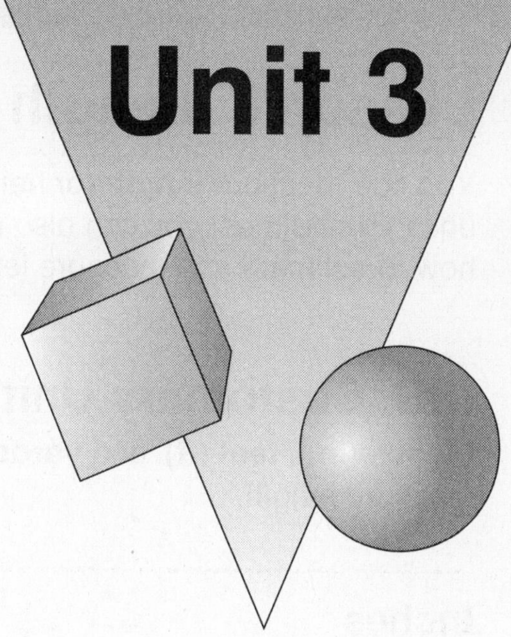

Measurement and Geometry

Look around you. Every object in the world can be measured in some way. You can measure the length of a shoe or how long you read at night. Everywhere you look, you also see shapes and solids. Whether it's the rectangular San Diego Chargers football field or the town square in Sonoma, California, there are circles, triangles, squares, rectangles, prisms, cylinders, spheres, and pyramids all around you.

In this unit, you will measure length using both the U.S. customary and metric systems. You will tell time using two kinds of clocks. You will also review shapes (flat figures) and solids (figures that have length, width, and height).

In This Unit

Lesson 8: Length

You can measure **length** (or height or distance) using U.S. customary or metric units. Sometimes, you can also use nonstandard units. This lesson will show you how to estimate and measure length. Round to the nearest unit in this lesson.

U.S. Customary Units of Length

Inches (in.), **feet (ft)**, and **yards (yd)** are some U.S. customary units used to measure length.

Inches

An inch is the smallest U.S. customary unit of length. To measure in inches, use an inch ruler, a tape measure, or a yardstick.

Example

How long is the following eraser to the nearest inch?

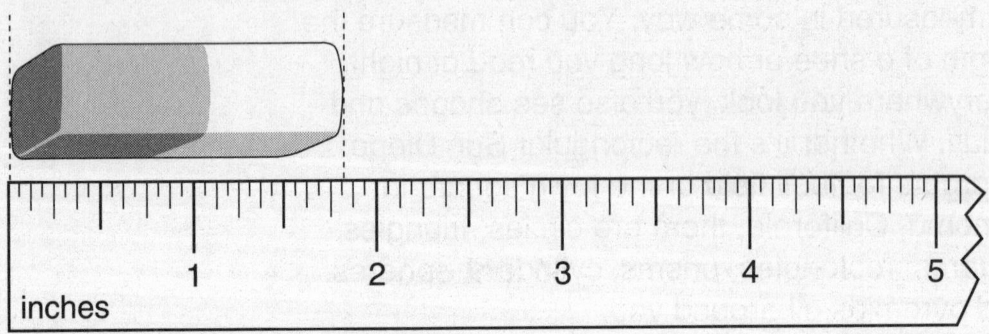

The eraser is about 2 inches long.

Content Standards: MG.1.1, MG.1.2

Feet and Yards

Feet and yards are U.S. customary units used to measure longer objects and distances. To measure in feet or yards, use an inch ruler, a tape measure, or a yardstick.

Example

A real-life egg carton is about 1 foot long.

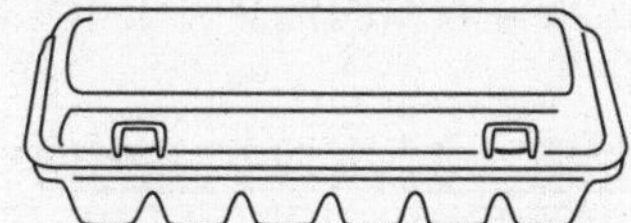

1 foot = 12 inches

Example

The distance from the top of a real-life bench to the ground is about 1 yard.

1 yard = 3 feet = 36 inches

The order of the lengths of the U.S. customary units from smallest to largest is inches, feet, yards.

You can compare different U.S. customary units of length by measuring the same object three times: in inches, feet, and yards.

Example

Will bought a roll of Extreme Bubble bubble gum tape. The wrapper said it had 3 yards of bubble gum. Will rolled out the bubble gum strip and measured it in inches with a ruler. It measured 108 inches long. He measured the bubble gum tape again, this time in feet. It measured 9 feet long.

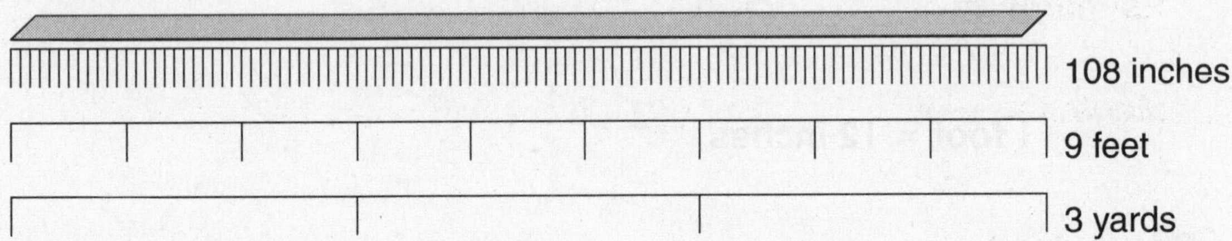

The length of Will's bubble gum strip is 108 inches or 9 feet or 3 yards.

It is usually best to measure an object with the unit that is closest to it in size. Small things should be measured in inches, and large things should be measured in feet or yards.

Example

Which is the best unit to measure a pencil?

Since a pencil is a small object, it is best to measure it using inches. A foot or a yard would be too big.

Content Standards: NS.6.1, MG.1.1, MG.1.3

Practice

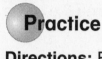

Directions: For Numbers 1 through 6, first look at the object to estimate the length in inches. Then measure the length in inches.

1. 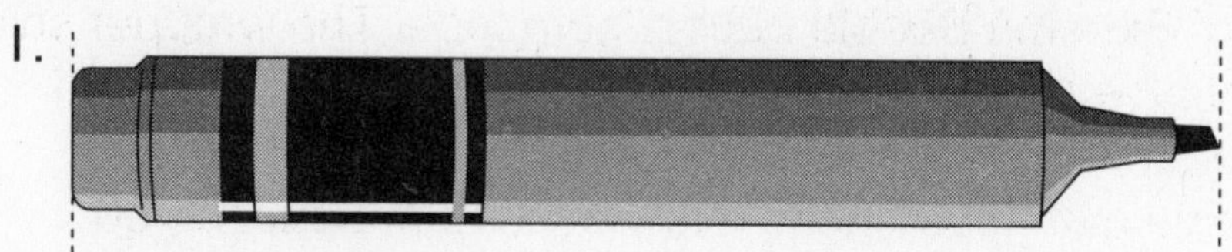

Estimate: about ______________ inches

Measurement: ______________ inches

2. 

Estimate: about ______________ inches

Measurement: ______________ inches

3. 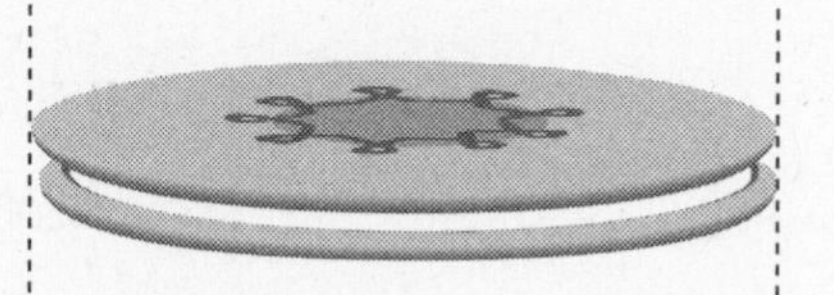

Estimate: about ______________ inches

Measurement: ______________ inches

4. 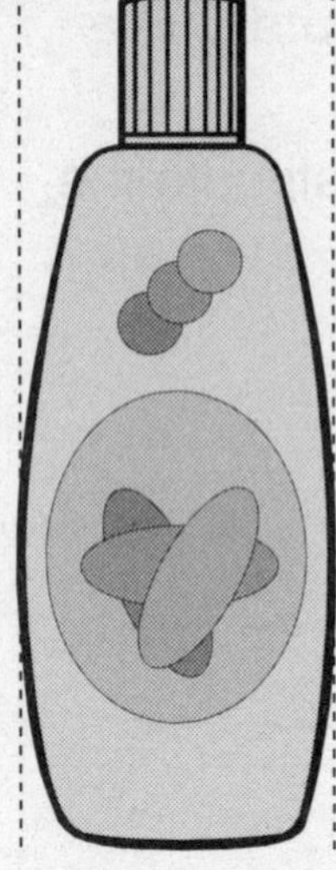

Estimate: about ______________ inches

Measurement: ______________ inches

5. 

Estimate: about ______________ inches

Measurement: ______________ inches

6. Your desktop.

Estimate: about ______________ inches

Measurement: ______________ inches

Content Standards: NS.6.1, MG.1.1, MG.1.2

7. Estimate the length of one of the walls of your classroom in yards. Then measure the length in yards.

   Estimate: about _______________ yards

   Measurement: _______________ yards

   Would it take a smaller or larger number of feet to measure the length of the same wall? Explain your answer.

   ____

   ____

   What is the measure of the wall in feet?

   Measurement: _______________ feet

8. In the real world, which object's length would you **most likely** measure in inches? Circle the correct answer.

9. Which is the **best** estimate for the height of a door?

   A. 24 inches

   B. 7 feet

   C. 1 yard

   D. 6 yards

10. Which is the **best** estimate for the length of a spoon?

   A. 2 inches

   B. 6 inches

   C. 3 feet

   D. 4 yards

Metric Units of Length

Centimeters (cm) and **meters (m)** are both metric units used to measure length.

Centimeters

A centimeter is about half as long as an inch. To measure in centimeters, use a centimeter ruler or a meterstick.

How long is the following piece of candy to the nearest centimeter?

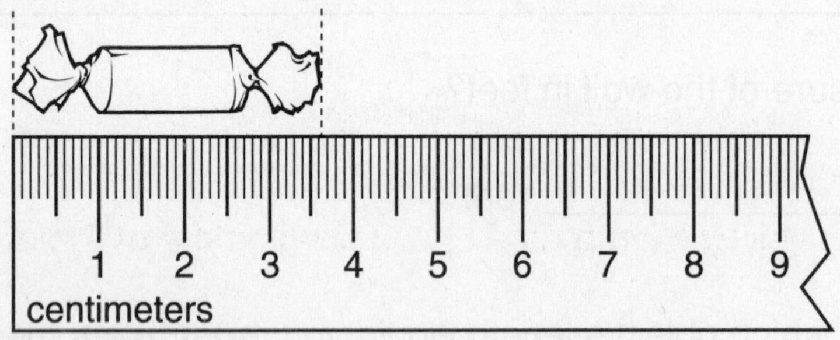

The piece of candy is about 4 centimeters long.

Meters

A meter is a metric unit used to measure longer objects and distances. To measure in meters, use a centimeter ruler or a meterstick.

A real-life baseball bat is about 1 meter long.

1 meter = 100 centimeters

The order of the lengths of the metric units from smallest to largest is centimeters, meters.

Content Standards: MG.1.1, MG.1.2

You can compare different metric units of length by measuring the same object twice: in centimeters and meters.

Example

Hailey has entered a jump rope contest. Jump ropes cannot be longer than 3 meters. Hailey uses a meterstick to measure her jump rope. It measures exactly 2 meters long.

To compare meters to centimeters, Hailey measures the jump rope again, this time in centimeters. It measures 200 centimeters long.

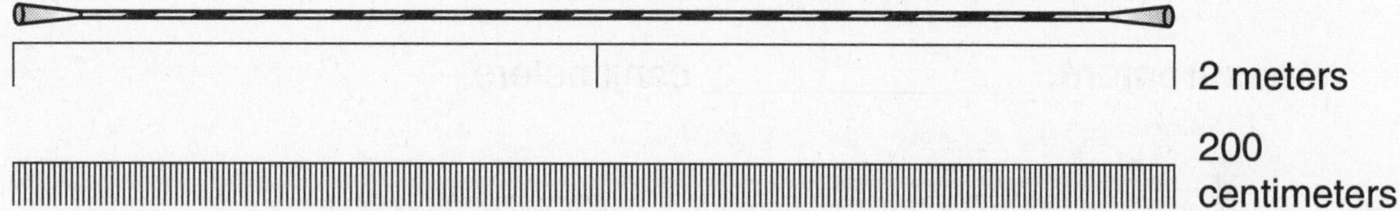

The length of Hailey's jump rope is 200 centimeters or 2 meters.

It is usually best to measure an object with the unit that is closest to it in size. Small things should be measured in centimeters, and large things should be measured in meters.

Example

Which is the best unit to measure an envelope?

Since an envelope is a small object, it is best to measure it using centimeters. A meter would be too big.

Practice

Directions: For Numbers 1 through 6, first look at the object to estimate the length in centimeters. Then measure the length in centimeters.

1.

Estimate: about ______________ centimeters

Measurement: ______________ centimeters

2.

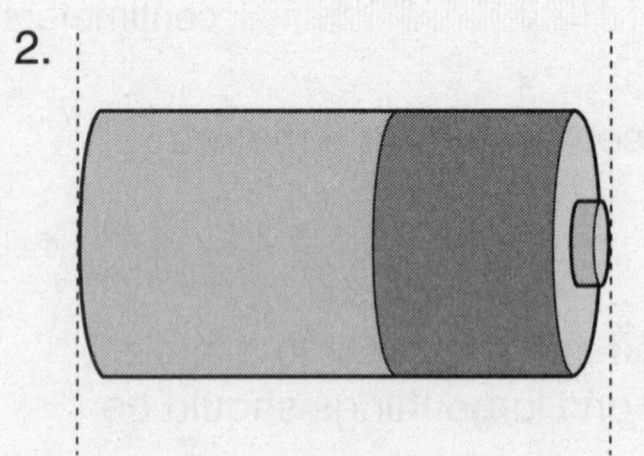

Estimate: about ______________ centimeters

Measurement: ______________ centimeters

3.

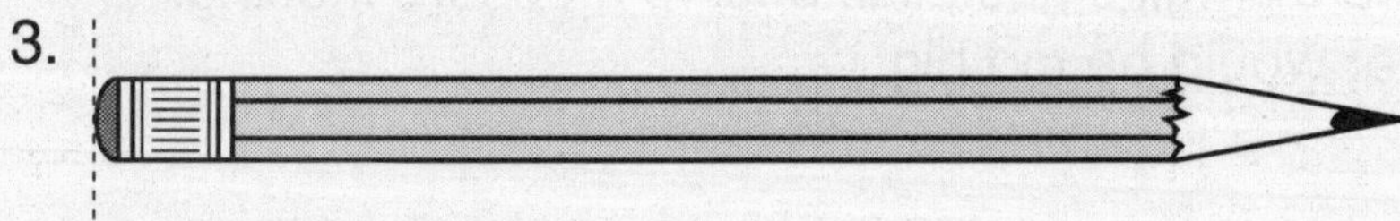

Estimate: about ______________ centimeters

Measurement: ______________ centimeters

4. 

Estimate: about ______________ centimeters

Measurement: ______________ centimeters

5. 

Estimate: about ______________ centimeters

Measurement: ______________ centimeters

6. The width of this book.

Estimate: about ______________ centimeters

Measurement: ______________ centimeters

7. Estimate the height of a bookshelf in your classroom in centimeters. Then measure the height in centimeters.

   Estimate: about _______________ centimeters

   Measurement: ________________ centimeters

   Would it take a smaller or larger number of meters to measure the height of the bookshelf? Explain your answer.

   ____

   ____

   What is the measure of the height of the bookshelf in meters?

   Measurement: ________________ meters

8. In the real world, which object's length would you **most likely** measure in meters? Circle the correct answer.

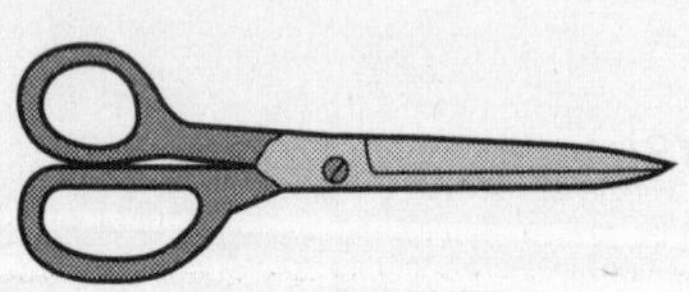
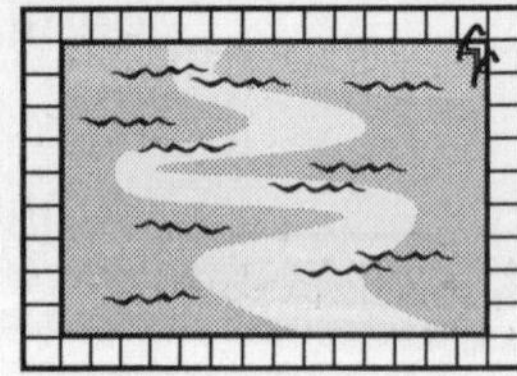
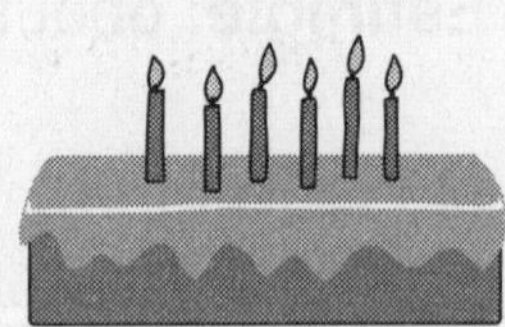

9. Which is the **best** estimate for the width of a door?

   A. 10 centimeters

   B. 1,000 centimeters

   C. 1 meter

   D. 10 meters

10. Which is the **best** estimate for the length of a crayon?

    A. 1 centimeter

    B. 10 centimeters

    C. 1 meter

    D. 10 meters

Content Standards: MG.1.1, MG.1.2

Nonstandard Units

U.S. customary and metric units are also called **standard units**. They mean the same thing to everyone, everywhere. But it is also possible to measure with **nonstandard units**.

Example

Measure the length of this pen using paper clips.

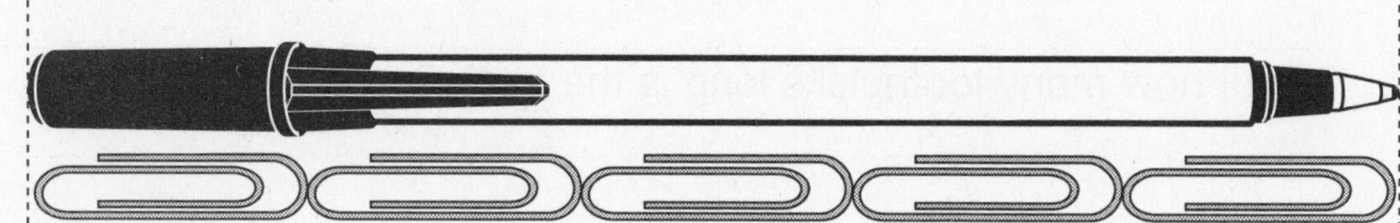

The pen is 5 paper clips long.

Now measure the pen again using buttons 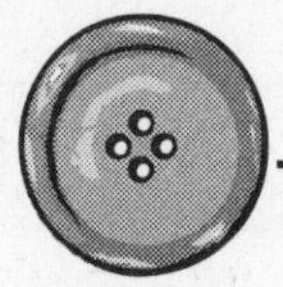.

Will you use a **greater** or **smaller** number of buttons than paper clips to measure the length of the pen?

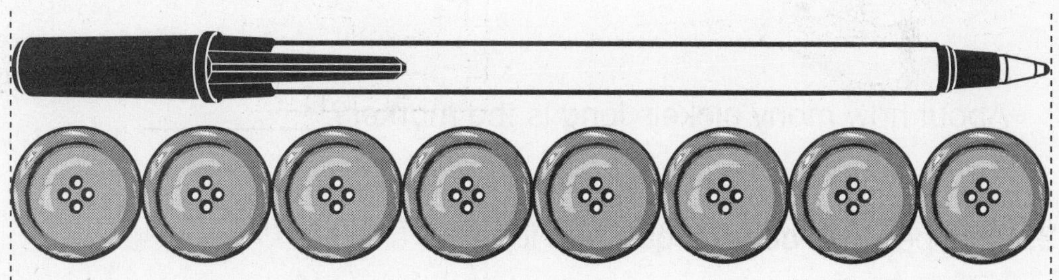

The pen is 8 buttons long.

You used a **greater** number of buttons than paper clips.

Practice

1. This straw is about 6 paper clips long.

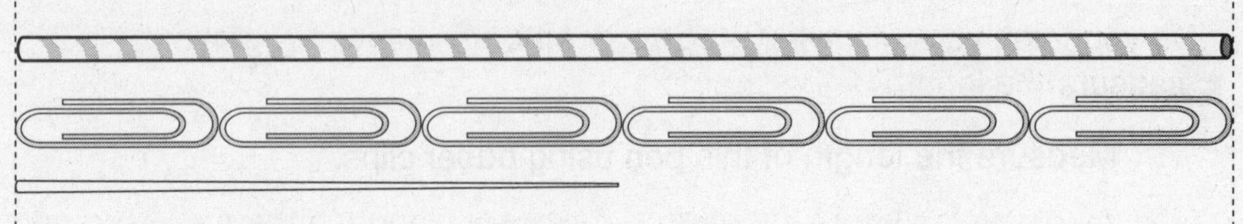

About how many toothpicks long is the straw? ________

2. This marker is about 3 screws long.

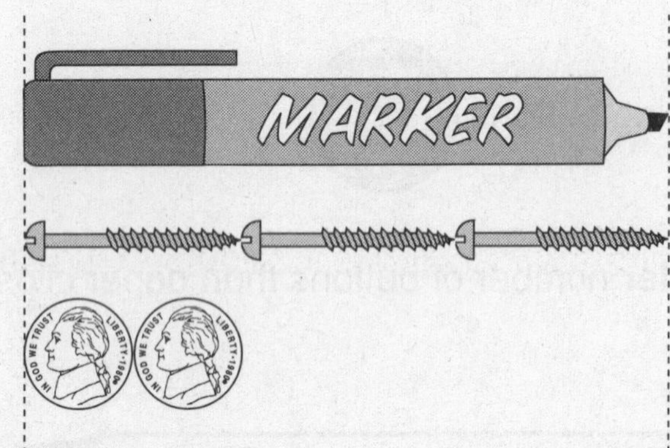

About how many nickels long is the marker? ________

3. This pencil is about 5 quarters long.

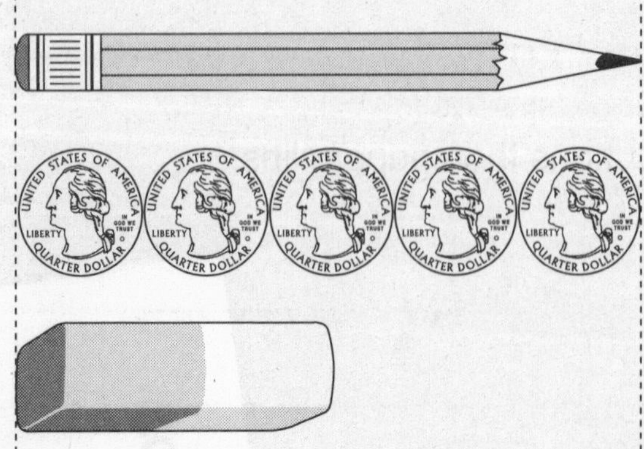

About how many erasers long is the pencil? ________

Content Standards: MG.1.1, MG.1.2

4. Measure the length of a shoe using a paper clip. Round to the nearest paper clip.

   The shoe is _________ paper clips long.

   Do you think you will use a **greater** or **smaller** number of crayons to measure the length of the shoe?

   ____

   Now measure the same shoe using a crayon. Round to the nearest crayon.

   The shoe is _________ crayons long.

   Was your guess correct? _________

5. Measure the length of a wall using a pencil. Round to the nearest pencil.

   The wall is _________ pencils long.

   Do you think you will use a **greater** or **smaller** number of folders to measure the length of the wall?

   ____

   Now measure the same wall using a folder.

   The wall is _________ folders long.

   Was your guess correct? _________

6. Johnny measured the length of his arm. First he measured it using pennies. Then he measured the length of his arm using dollar bills.

   Did Johnny use more pennies or dollar bills? ____________________

   Explain your answer. ____

   ____

Practice Questions

1

a piece of chalk

Ⓐ

the top to the bottom of a folder

Ⓒ

the top of your desk

Ⓑ

the chalkboard

Ⓓ

2

centimeter Ⓐ

meter Ⓑ

foot Ⓒ

yard Ⓓ

3

the length of your foot

Ⓐ

the width of a piece of hair

Ⓒ

the length of your arm

Ⓑ

the width of your finger

Ⓓ

4

18 meters

Ⓐ

180 centimeters

Ⓒ

18 centimeters

Ⓑ

180 meters

Ⓓ

5

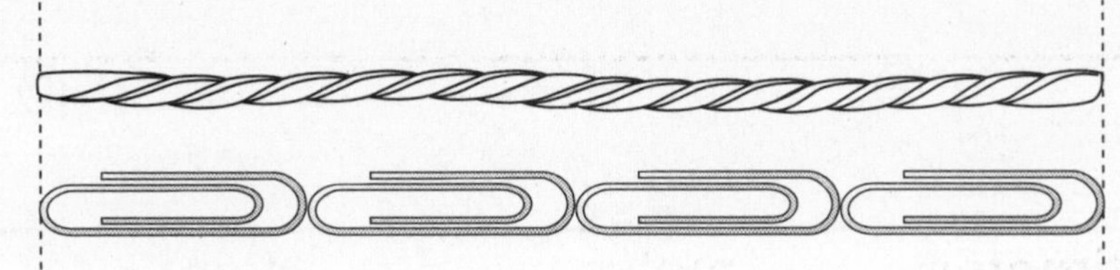

Ⓐ

Ⓒ

Ⓑ

Ⓓ

6

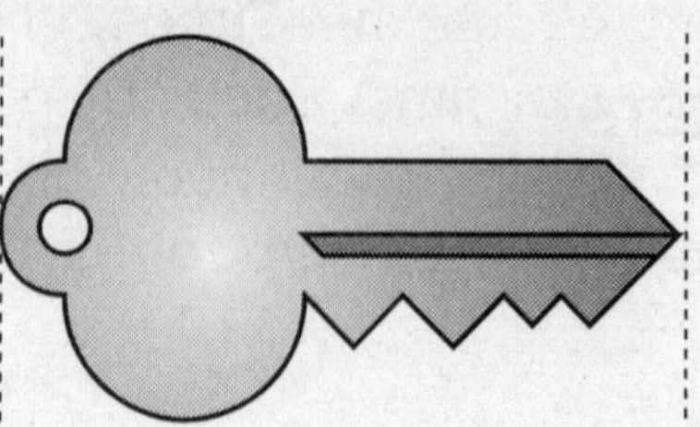

1 centimeter

Ⓐ

10 centimeters

Ⓒ

5 centimeters

Ⓑ

20 centimeters

Ⓓ

7

3 inches	3 yards	3 feet	3 meters
Ⓐ	Ⓑ	Ⓒ	Ⓓ

Content Standards: MG.1.4

Lesson 9: Time

In this lesson, you will learn about time. **Time** can be measured in **hours** and **minutes**. Clocks are used to tell time. Each day has 24 hours. There are 12 hours before noon and 12 hours after noon. To tell time **from midnight up to noon**, use **A.M.** To tell time **from noon up to midnight**, use **P.M.**

Digital Clocks

On a **digital clock**, the number before the colon (:) shows the hour. The number after the colon shows the minutes. A digital clock shows A.M. and P.M. with a little light by the A.M. or P.M.

Example

What time does the following clock show?

The light is on by the A.M. The time is 10:30 A.M.

Example

What time does the following clock show?

The light is on by the P.M. The time is 9:15 P.M.

Analog Clocks

The numbers on an **analog** or **dial clock** show the hours. The little marks around the outside of the clock show the minutes. From one number to the next there are 5 minutes. There are 60 minutes in each hour. Most analog clocks do not show A.M. or P.M.

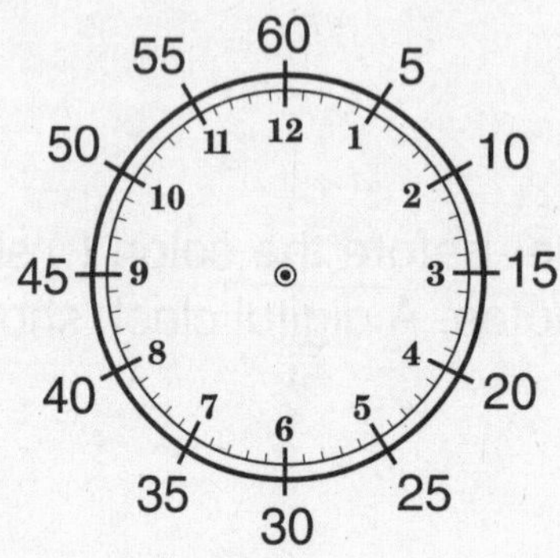

Example

What time does the following clock show? (It is between noon and midnight.)

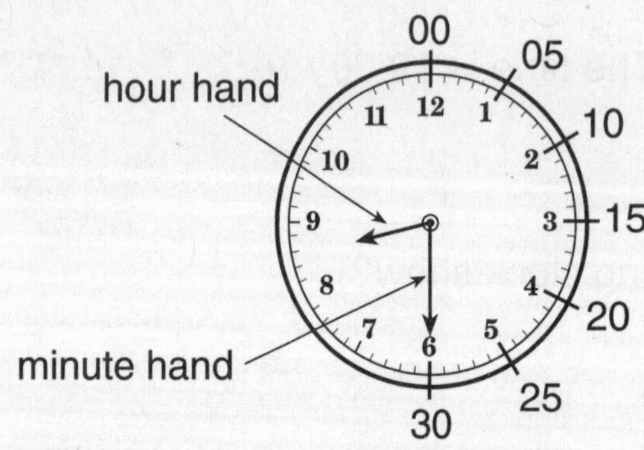

The **short hand** is called the **hour hand**. It points to the **hour**. If the hour hand is pointing between two numbers, the hour is the last number it passed as it went around the clock. In this example, the hour hand has passed 8 and is pointing between the 8 and 9. This means the hour is 8.

The **long hand** is called the **minute hand**. It points to the **minute**. It is pointing to the 6. This means it is 30 minutes past the hour.

It is given that it is between noon and midnight. This means it is P.M. time.

The time is 8:30 P.M.

Content Standards: MG.1.4

Practice

Directions: For Numbers 1 through 6, write the time shown on each analog clock. Be sure to include A.M. or P.M.

1. It is between noon and midnight.

____

4. It is between noon and midnight.

____

2. It is between midnight and noon.

____

5. It is between midnight and noon.

____

3. It is between midnight and noon.

____

6. It is between noon and midnight.

____

Directions: For Numbers 7 through 14, write the time shown on each digital clock. Be sure to include A.M. or P.M.

7. 

____

8. 

____

9. 

____

10. 

____

11. 

____

12. 

____

13. 

____

14. 

____

Content Standards: MG.1.4

Hours, Half Hours, Quarter Hours

The following table lists some reminders that may be helpful when telling time using minutes, quarter hours, half hours, or hours.

Reminders
$\frac{1}{4}$ hour = 15 minutes
$\frac{1}{2}$ hour = 30 minutes
$\frac{3}{4}$ hour = 45 minutes
1 hour = 60 minutes

Examples

6:00 is read as:

"six o'clock"

6:15 can be read as:

"six fifteen"

"fifteen minutes after six"

"a quarter after six"

6:30 can be read as:

"six thirty"

"thirty minutes after six"

"half past six"

6:45 can be read as:

"six forty-five"

"forty-five minutes after six"

"fifteen minutes before **seven**"

"a quarter to **seven**"

Practice

Directions: For Numbers 1 through 6, write the time shown on the clock in two different ways. Be sure to include A.M. or P.M.

1. It is between noon and midnight.

____

____

2. It is between midnight and noon.

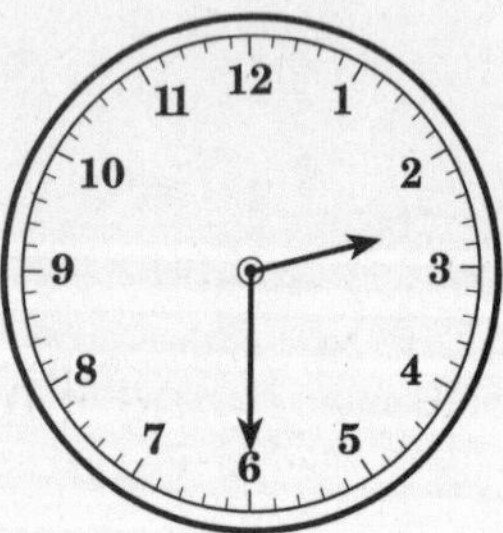

____

____

3. 

____

____

4. It is between noon and midnight.

____

____

5. It is between midnight and noon.

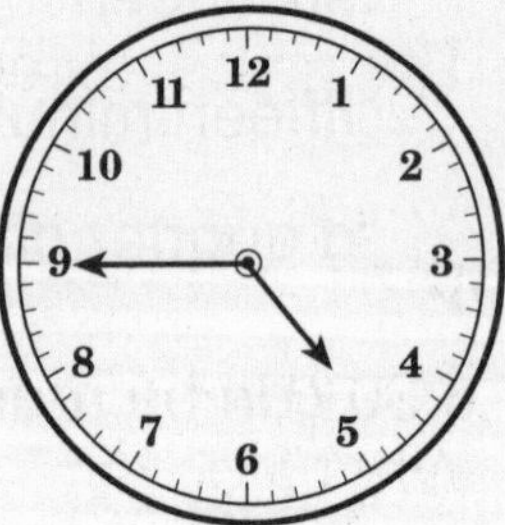

____

____

6. 

____

____

Content Standards: MG.1.5

Elapsed Time

Elapsed time is how much time has passed from one time to another.

Example

Use the two clocks shown to find out how long the game lasted.

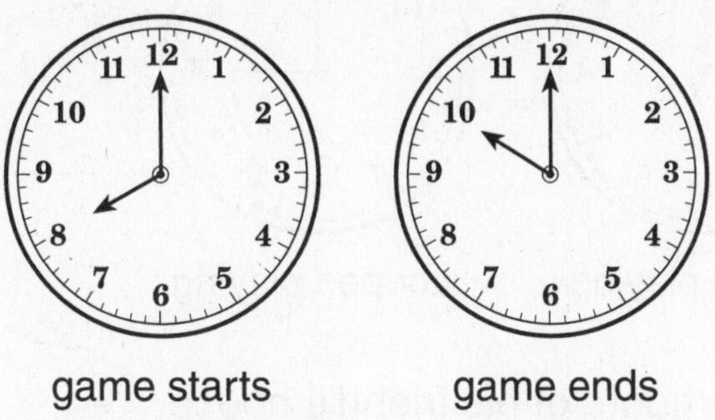

game starts game ends

The game started at 8:00. It ended at 10:00. Count the number of hours from 8:00 to 10:00.

Start with 8:00. 1 hour later is 9:00. 1 more hour is 10:00. There are 2 hours from 8:00 to 10:00.

The game lasted 2 hours.

Example

Tasha went to her aunt's house at 3:00. She got home 4 hours later. What time did Tasha get home?

Start at the 3. Count 4 hours around the clock.

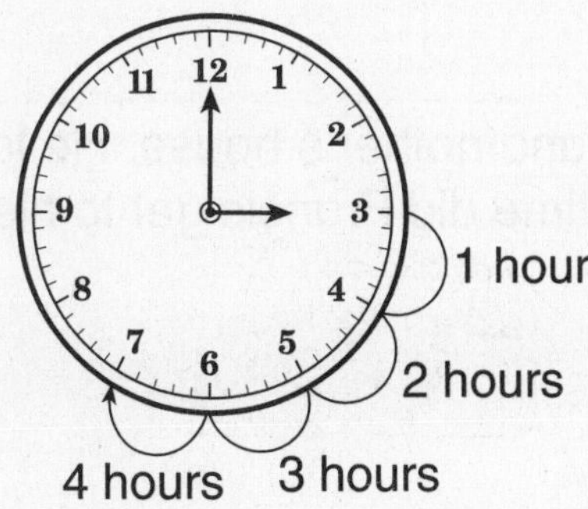

Tasha got home at 7:00.

Practice

1. Andy started playing at his friend's house at 10:00. He went home at 3:00. How many hours did Andy play at his friend's house?

started playing stopped playing

Andy played for ___________ hours at his friend's house.

2. Mary practiced her trumpet for 2 hours on Saturday. She started practicing at 2:00. What time did Mary finish practicing? Draw the hands on the clock to show the time Mary finished practicing.

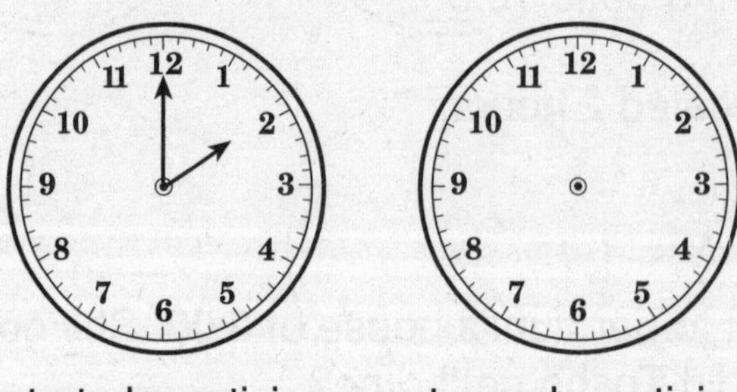

started practicing stopped practicing

Mary finished practicing at ___________.

3. Francis drove from Los Angeles to his grandmother's house. He left at 8:00 A.M. and arrived 5 hours later. What time did Francis get to his grandmother's house?

____

4. Measure the amount of time that has passed. ____________

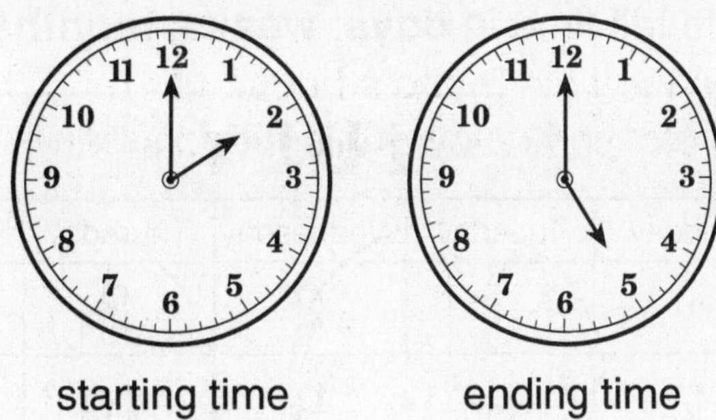

Directions: The following clocks show the time that each student started and finished his or her homework. Use them to answer Numbers 5 and 6.

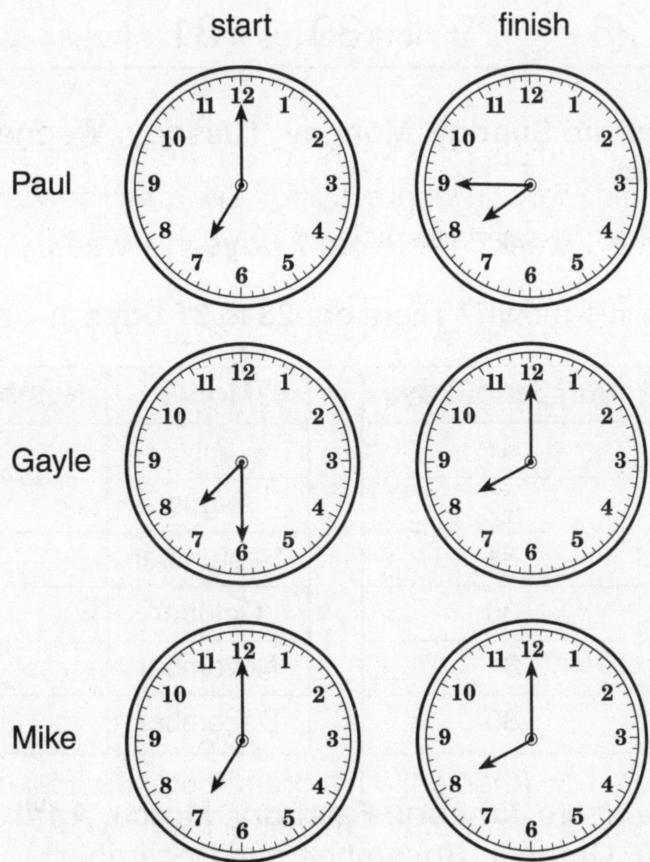

5. Who took the **longest** to complete his or her homework? __________

6. Who took the **shortest** to complete his or her homework? __________

Days, Weeks, Months, and Years

Calendars are used to tell time in **days**, **weeks**, **months**, and **years**.

JULY						
Sunday	Monday	Tuesday	Wednesday	Thursday	Friday	Saturday
		1	2	3	4	5
6	7	8	9	10	11	12
13	14	15	16	17	18	19
20	21	22	23	24	25	26
27	28	29	30	31		

The days of the week are **Sunday**, **Monday**, **Tuesday**, **Wednesday**, **Thursday**, **Friday**, and **Saturday**.

How many days are in 1 week? There are **7 days** in **1 week**.

How many days are in 1 month? There are **28** to **31 days** in **1 month**.

Month	Number of Days
January	31
February	28
March	31
April	30
May	31
June	30

Month	Number of Days
July	31
August	31
September	30
October	31
November	30
December	31

The months of the year are **January**, **February**, **March**, **April**, **May**, **June**, **July**, **August**, **September**, **October**, **November**, and **December**.

How many months are in 1 year? There are **12 months** in **1 year**.

How many days, weeks, and months are in 1 year? There are **365 days**, **52 weeks**, or **12 months** in **1 year**.

TIP: Sometimes February has 29 days. This happens every 4 years (leap year). The year 2004 was a leap year.

Content Standards: MG.1.4

Practice

1. Complete the calendar to show this month.

Month: ______						
Sunday	Monday	Tuesday	Wednesday	Thursday	Friday	Saturday

2. How many days are in this month? ______

3. What day of the week is today? ______

4. What is the date of the last Friday of this month?

______

5. What is the date of the second Tuesday of this month?

______

6. On what day is the 4th of this month? ______

7. On what day is the 21st of this month? ______

8. Darian's brother is 1 year old. How many **months** old is Darian's brother?

____

9. Nick has been at camp for 2 weeks. How many **days** has Nick been at camp?

____

Directions: Use the calendars below for Numbers 10 through 12.

FEBRUARY						
Sun.	Mon.	Tues.	Wed.	Thurs.	Fri.	Sat.
				1	2	3
4	5	6	7	8	9	10
11	12	13	14	15	16	17
18	19	20	21	22	23	24
25	26	27	28			

MARCH						
Sun.	Mon.	Tues.	Wed.	Thurs.	Fri.	Sat.
				1	2	3
4	5	6	7	8	9	10
11	12	13	14	15	16	17
18	19	20	21	22	23	24
25	26	27	28	29	30	31

10. Valentine's Day is on February 14. On what day of the week is Valentine's Day?

____

11. Jane's birthday is on the last day of February. What is the date of Jane's birthday?

A. February 28

B. February 29

C. February 30

D. February 31

12. Anna went to the art museum on the third Monday in March. On what date did Anna go to the art museum?

A. March 11

B. March 12

C. March 18

D. March 19

Practice Questions

1

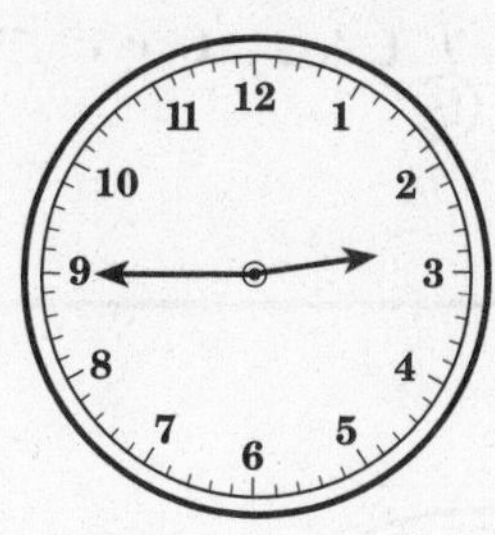

Ⓐ

Ⓒ

Ⓑ

Ⓓ

2

11:30

Ⓐ

Ⓑ

Ⓒ

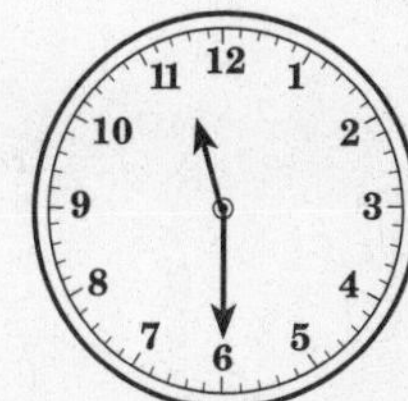

Ⓓ

3

January	February	June	November
Ⓐ	Ⓑ	Ⓒ	Ⓓ

4

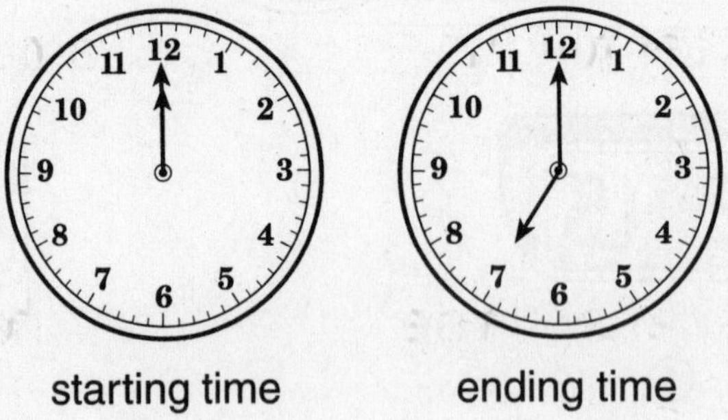

starting time ending time

5 hours	7 hours	10 hours	12 hours
Ⓐ	Ⓑ	Ⓒ	Ⓓ

5

12	30	52	365
Ⓐ	Ⓑ	Ⓒ	Ⓓ

6

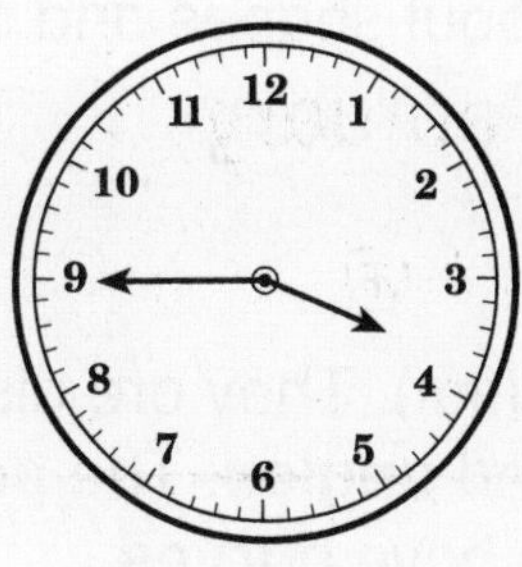

a quarter to four
Ⓐ

a quarter after four
Ⓒ

a quarter after three
Ⓑ

half past three
Ⓓ

7

Friday	Wednesday	Monday	Sunday
Ⓐ	Ⓑ	Ⓒ	Ⓓ

8

10:00 A.M. 1:00 P.M.	9	5	3	1
	Ⓐ	Ⓑ	Ⓒ	Ⓓ

Lesson 10: Geometric Figures

In this lesson, you will learn about shapes and solid figures.

Shapes

Shapes are two-dimensional (flat). They are also called **plane figures**. Most shapes have **sides** (edges) and **angles**. The point where two sides meet is called a **vertex**. Other shapes have **curves**.

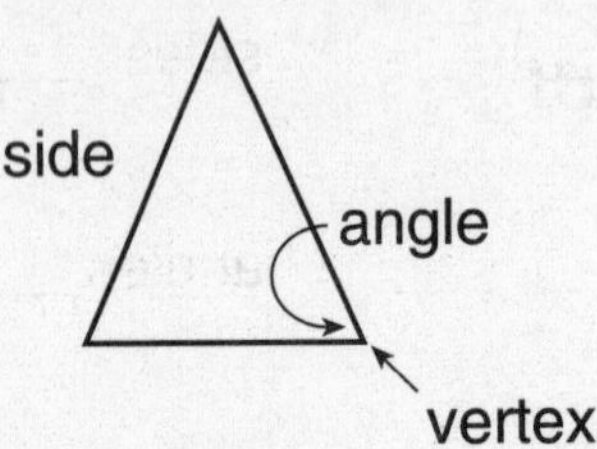

Here are some two-dimensional shapes:

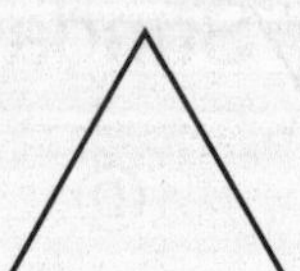

A **circle** is a round shape and has
0 sides (edges)
0 angles
0 vertices

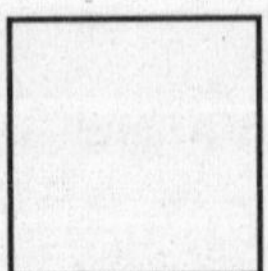

A **triangle** has
3 sides (edges)
3 angles
3 vertices

A **square** has
4 equal sides (edges)
4 equal angles
4 vertices

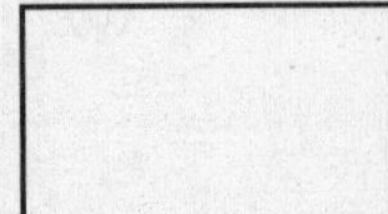

A **rectangle** has
4 sides (edges)
4 equal angles
4 vertices

Content Standards: MG.2.1

Practice

1. Count the sides, angles, and vertices of each shape.

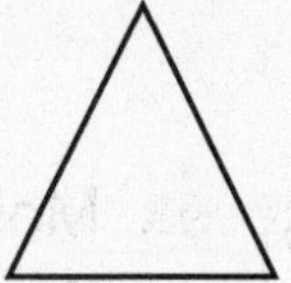
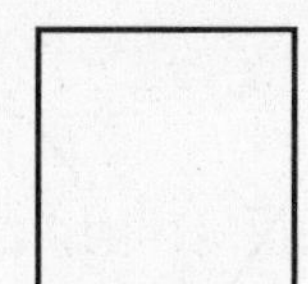

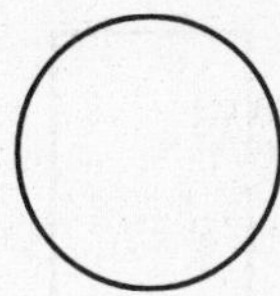

sides ______	sides ______	sides ______	sides ______
angles ______	angles ______	angles ______	angles ______
vertices ______	vertices ______	vertices ______	vertices ______

2. Draw a line from each real-world object to the shape it reminds you of.

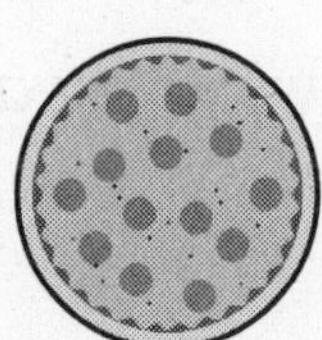

rectangle   circle   triangle   square

3. Color the shape that has 3 sides.

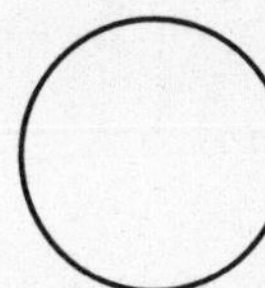
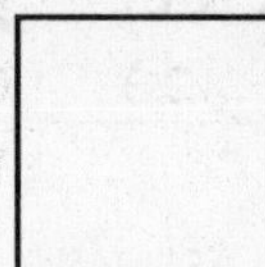
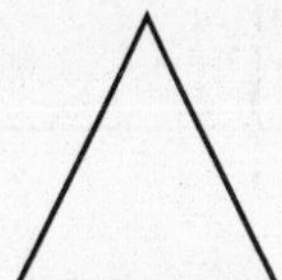

Directions: For Numbers 4 through 7, read the sentence. Then write the letter of each figure that matches the sentence. You may have more than one answer.

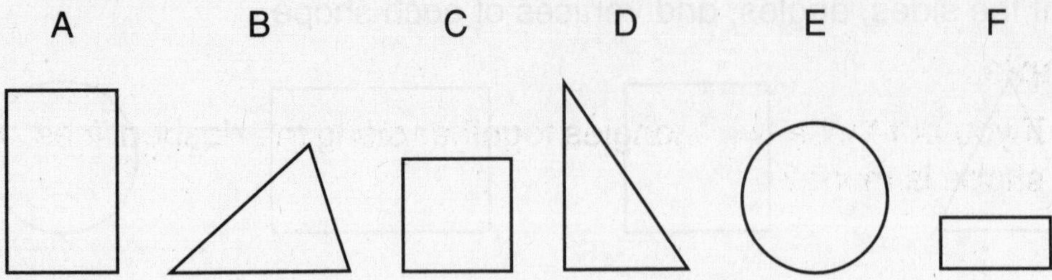

4. It has no sides or angles. ____________

5. It is a triangle. ____________

6. It has four sides and four angles. ____________

7. It is a square. ____________

8. Name one way a square and a rectangle are alike and one way they are different.

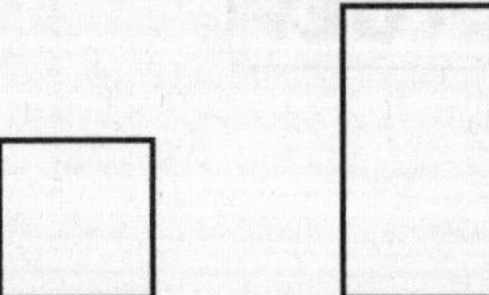

Alike ____

____

Different ____

____

Content Standards: MG.2.2

Putting Shapes Together

Two or more shapes can be put together to make a single shape.

Example

If you put these two triangles together along the dashed lines, what shape is made?

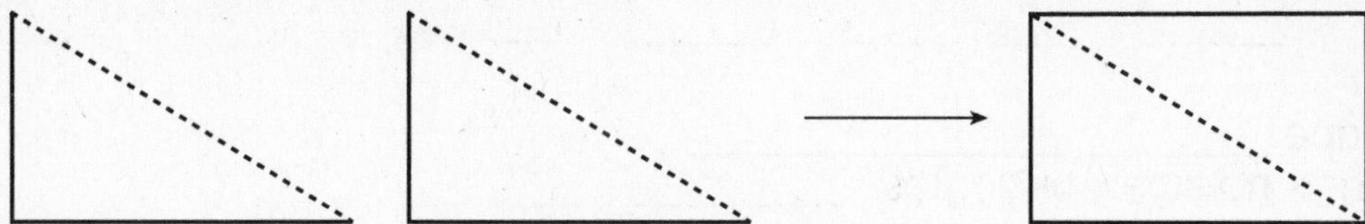

The two triangles can be put together to make a rectangle.

Cutting Shapes Apart

A shape can be cut apart to make two or more shapes.

Example

If you cut this square apart at the dashed line, what two shapes are made?

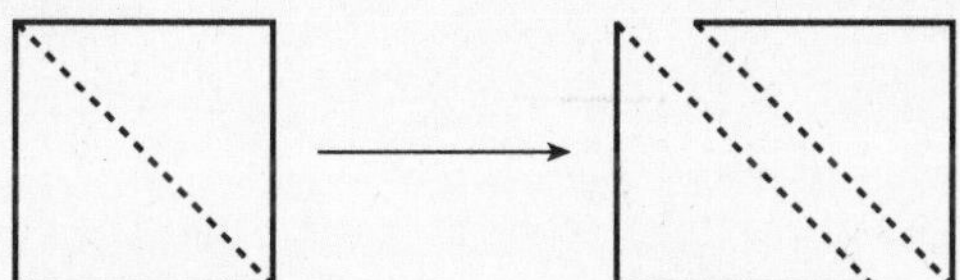

This square can be cut apart to make two triangles.

Practice

Directions: For Numbers 1 and 2, draw the shape that is made if the given shapes are put together at the dashed lines. Then write the name of the shape.

1. →

shape ______________________

2.

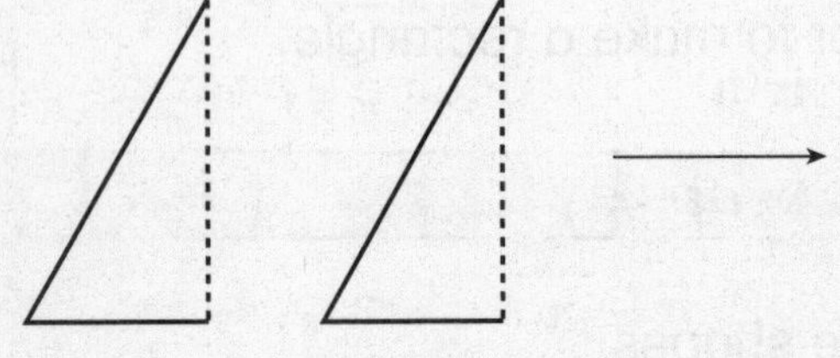

shape ______________________

Directions: For Numbers 3 and 4, draw the shapes that are made if the given shape is cut apart at the dashed lines. Then write the name of the shapes.

3.

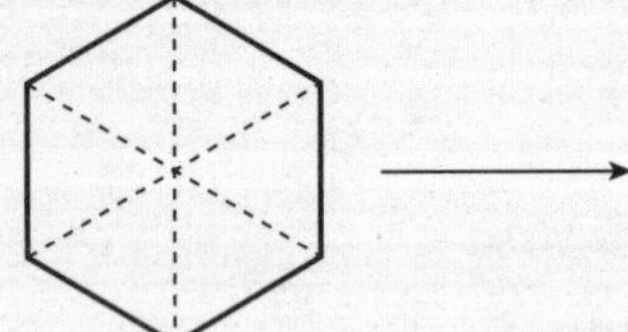

shapes ______________________

4.

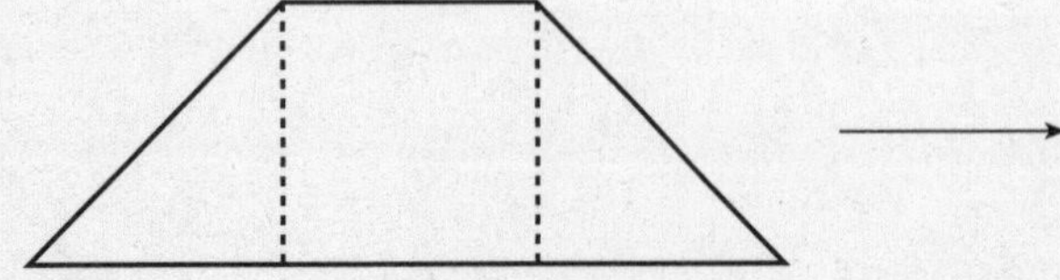

shapes ______________________

Content Standards: MG.2.1

Solid Figures

Solid figures are not flat, and they have three dimensions (length, width, and height). Some solid figures have all flat surfaces and no curves. Other solid figures have curves.

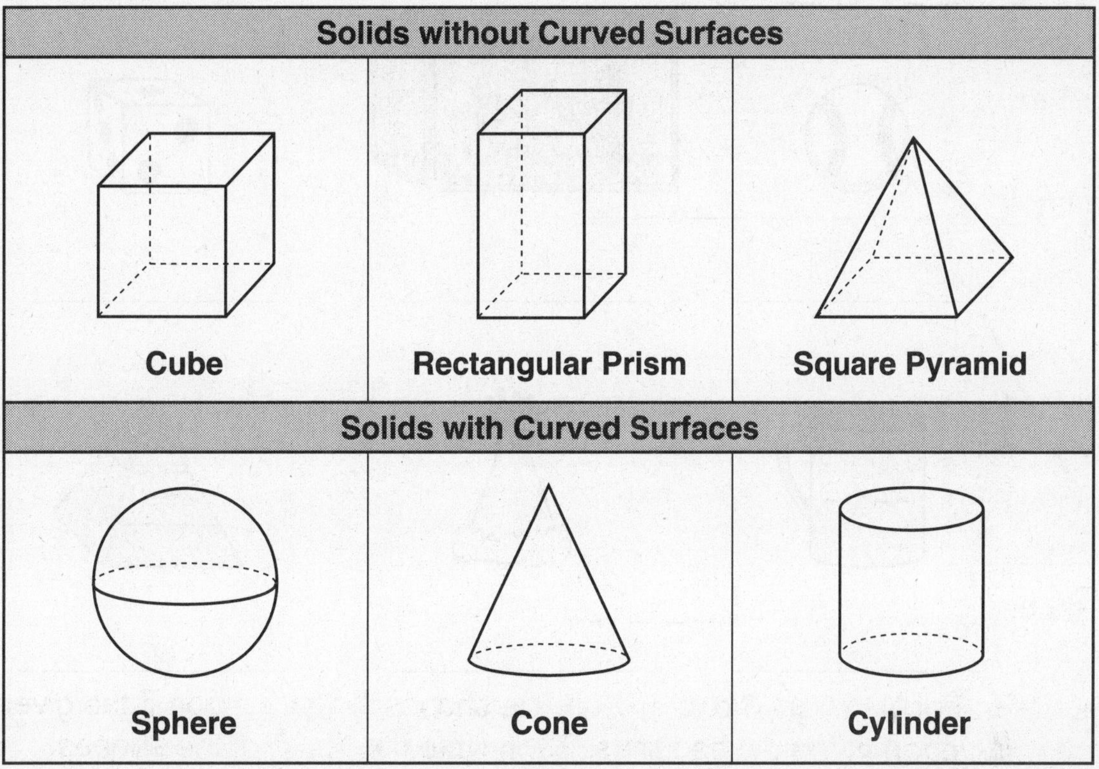

Faces, Edges, and Vertices

Solid figures without curves have **faces**, **edges**, and **vertices**.

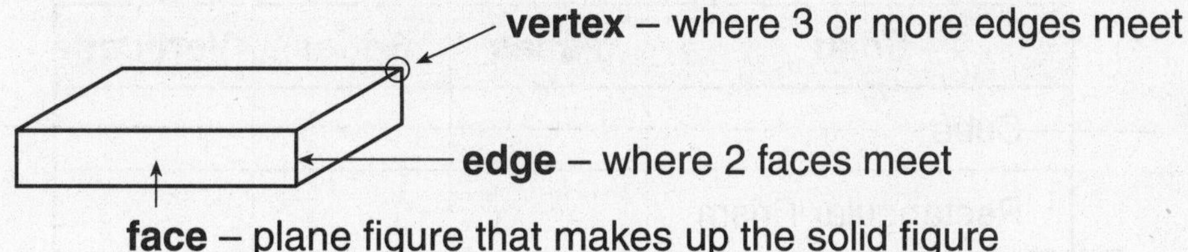

Practice

1. Write the name of each solid figure under the object that it looks like the most.

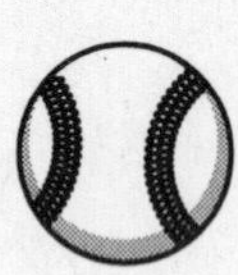

______________ ______________ ______________

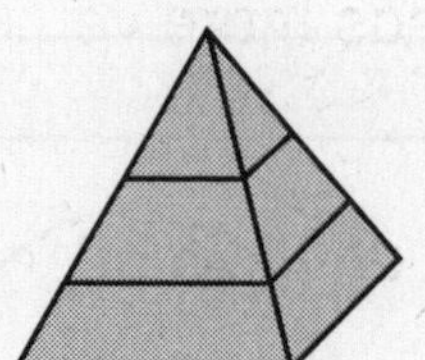

______________ ______________ ______________

2. What solid figure has no flat surfaces? ______________

3. Complete the table with the correct number of faces, edges, and vertices for each solid figure.

Solid	Faces	Edges	Vertices
Cube			
Rectangular Prism			
Square Pyramid			

Content Standards: MG.2.1

Directions: For Numbers 4 through 6, read the sentence. Then write the letter of each figure that matches the sentence. You may have more than one answer.

A

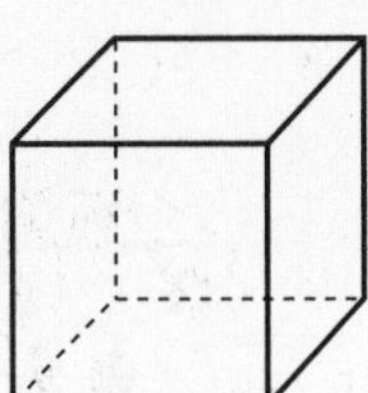

B

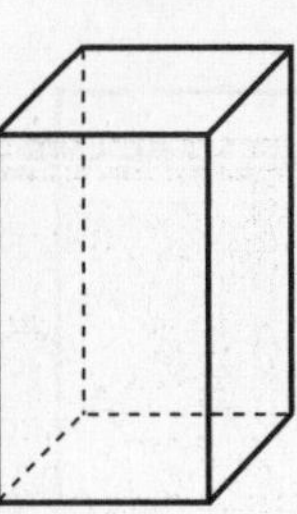

C

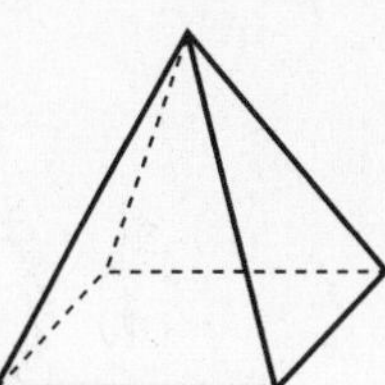

4. Some of its faces are triangles. ____________________

5. It has more vertices than faces. ____________________

6. It has eight edges. ____________________

7. How are a cube and a square pyramid **different**?

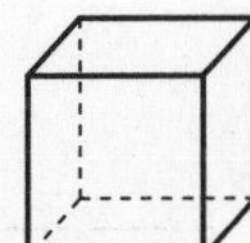

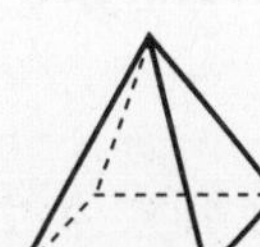

____

____

____

Practice Questions

1

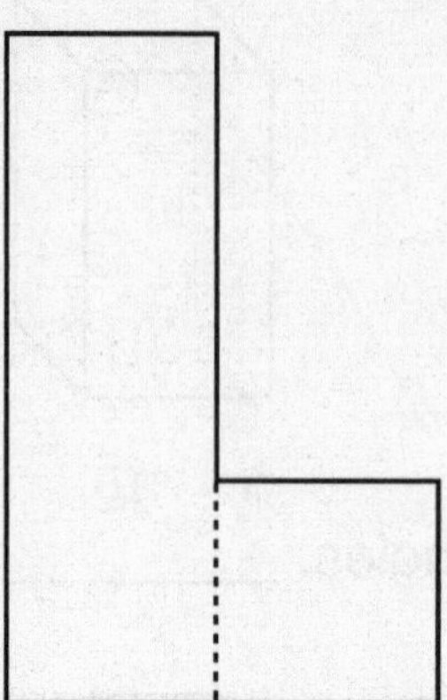

square and circle
Ⓐ

square and triangle
Ⓑ

rectangle and triangle
Ⓒ

rectangle and square
Ⓓ

2

cone
Ⓐ

cube
Ⓑ

sphere
Ⓒ

square pyramid
Ⓓ

3

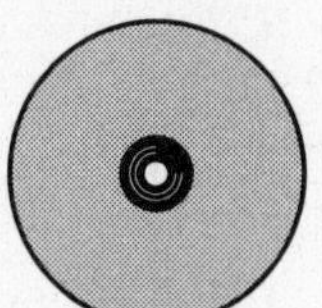

circle Ⓐ

triangle Ⓒ

square Ⓑ

rectangle Ⓓ

4

1 Ⓐ

3 Ⓑ

4 Ⓒ

6 Ⓓ

5

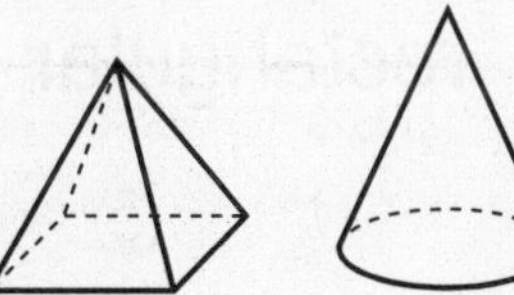

Ⓐ

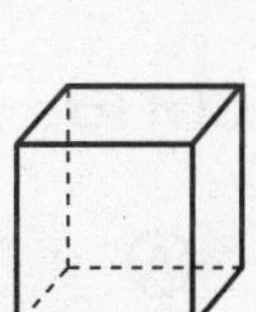

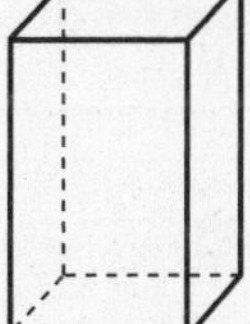

Ⓒ

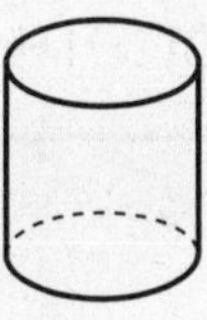

Ⓑ

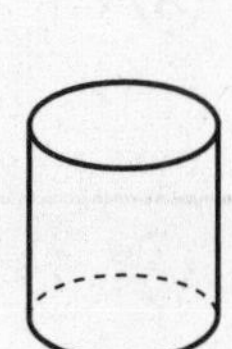

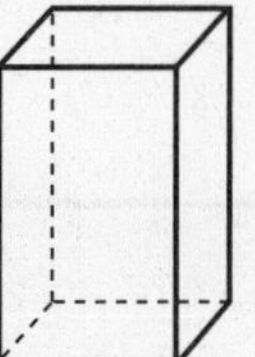

Ⓓ

6

Ⓐ

Ⓑ

Ⓒ

Ⓓ

7

cone
Ⓐ

square pyramid
Ⓑ

rectangular prism
Ⓒ

cube
Ⓓ

8

4 Ⓐ

6 Ⓑ

8 Ⓒ

12 Ⓓ

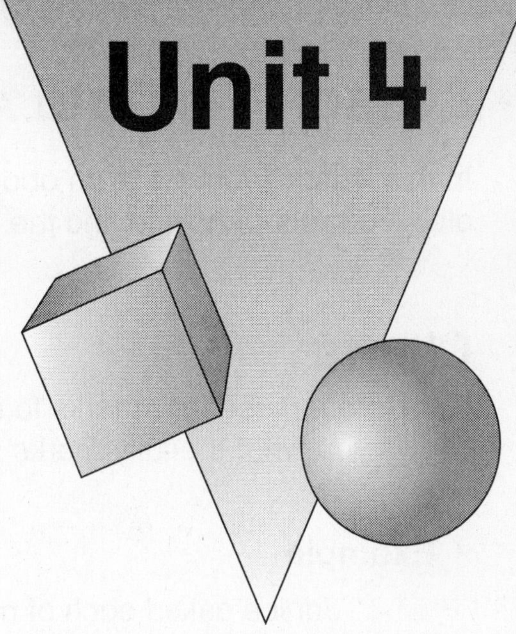

Statistics, Data Analysis, and Probability

Numbers are used to tell about everything around us. They can be used to tell how many people live in different parts of California, how to find a hotel in San José, or what chance there is that it will rain tomorrow.

In this unit, you will read charts, pictographs, and bar graphs. You will also get to make some graphs yourself. Finally, you will find the mode and range of some data sets.

In This Unit

Data Analysis

Lesson 11: Data Analysis

In this lesson, you will learn about ways to show information, or **data**. You will also learn about how to find the mode and range of a set of data.

Charts

Charts often use tally marks to show how many of something there are. The **key** shows you what the tally marks stand for.

Example

Janice asked each of her classmates what his or her favorite fruit is. Each time one of her classmates answered, she put a tally mark by that type of fruit. At the end, she counted the tally marks for each kind of fruit. The following chart shows her results.

Favorite Fruit

Fruit	Tally	Count
banana	𝍸 |	6
strawberry	𝍸	5
cherry	|	1
apple	||	2
orange	|	1

KEY

| = 1 student vote

𝍸 = 5 student votes

How many of Janice's classmates chose strawberries?

Look under the "Fruit" column for a strawberry. Look across that row. The table shows that 5 of Janice's classmates chose strawberries.

Content Standards: AF.1.3, P.1.1, P.1.4

Practice

Directions: Use the following information to answer Numbers 1 through 5.

Travis asked his friends which of the following California cities they have visited. His results are shown in the chart below.

California Cities Visited

City	Tally	Count
Bakersfield	||||	4
Fresno	|||	3
Salinas	~~||||~~ ||||	9
Santa Rosa	~~||||~~	5

1. Which city have the **most** people visited? ______________

2. Which city have the **least** people visited? ______________

3. How many people have visited Bakersfield? ______________

4. How many more people have visited Salinas than have visited Bakersfield?

____

5. How many more people have visited Santa Rosa than have visited Fresno?

____

6. Ask your classmates which of the following places they would most like to go on a vacation: mountains, an ocean, a desert, or a lake. Tally each answer in the following chart. Then write in the total count for places.

Places to Visit on Vacation

Place	Tally	Count
mountains		
ocean		
desert		
lake		

KEY

| = 1 student

卌 = 5 students

Directions: Use the chart you made in Number 6 to answer Numbers 7 through 11.

7. How many students chose mountains as the place they would like to go?

____

8. How many students chose a desert as the place they would like to go?

____

9. What is the difference between the number of students that chose an ocean and the number of students that chose a lake?

____

10. Order the places from the place that the **greatest** number of people said they would like to visit to the place that the **least** number of people said they would like to visit.

____

11. Compare your chart with a classmate's chart. Are they the same? Explain why they are the same or why they are different.

____

Content Standards: P.1.2, P.1.4

Pictographs

Pictographs (or picture graphs) use pictures to show how many of something there are. Most pictographs have a key that shows what each picture stands for.

Example

Janice made the following pictograph from the chart on page 140.

Favorite Fruit

banana	
strawberry	
cherry	
apple	
orange	

KEY

= 1 student

How many of Janice's classmates chose bananas?

The pictograph shows 6 pictures in the banana row. The key shows that each picture stands for 1 student. So 6 students chose bananas as their favorite fruit.

Practice

Directions: Use the following information to answer Numbers 1 through 4.

The pictograph below shows the number of [book] read by second graders each week.

Books Read by Second Graders

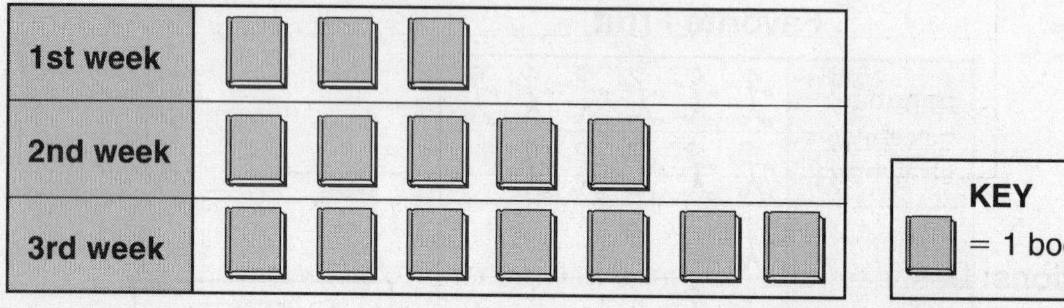

1. How many more books did the second graders read in the 3rd week than in the 1st week?

   ____

2. Add the number of books read each week. How many total books did the second graders read in the three weeks?

   ____

3. During which week did the second graders read 5 books? ________

4. Which statement about the information in the pictograph is **not true**?

   A. Three books were read in the 1st week.

   B. The greatest number of books was read in the 3rd week.

   C. Two more books were read in the 1st week than were read in the 2nd week.

   D. Two more books were read in the 3rd week than were read in the 2nd week.

Content Standards: P.1.2, P.1.4

5. Look at the eye colors of 20 people. Mark each person's eye color in the following chart with a tally. Then write in the total count for each eye color.

Eye Colors

Color of Eyes	Tally	Count
Brown		
Blue		
Green		
Other		

KEY
| = 1
𝍸 = 5

Directions: Use the chart you made in Number 5 to answer Numbers 6 through 9.

6. Make a pictograph of the information.

Eye Colors

brown	
blue	
green	
other	

KEY
(half eye) = 1 person
(eye) = 2 people

7. Which eye color did the **most** people have? ________________

8. Which eye color did the **fewest** people have? ________________

9. If you look at the eye color of one more person, what eye color do you think he or she will have? Explain your answer.

____

____

Bar Graphs

Bar graphs use bars to compare information. The bars can go up from the bottom to the top or across from the left to the right. By looking at the heights or lengths of the bars, you can quickly compare the information in a bar graph.

Example

Janice made the following bar graph from the information in the chart on page 140.

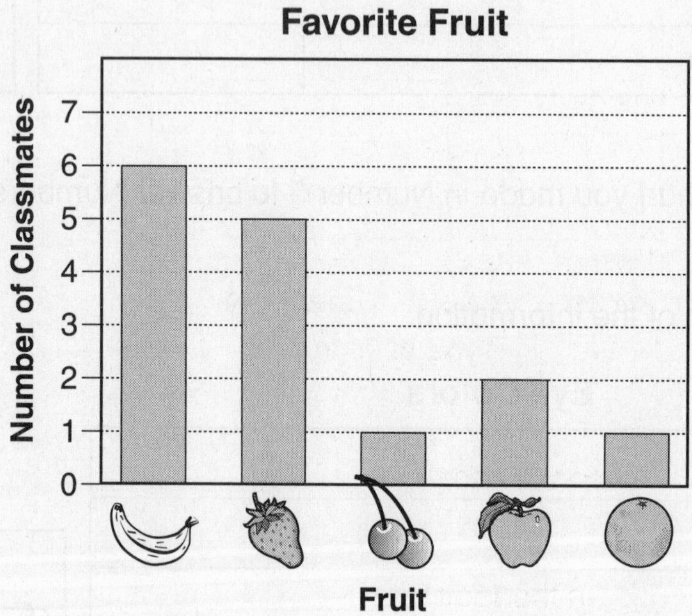

How many of Janice's classmates chose apples?

Look along the bottom of the graph until you find the picture of the apple. Put your finger on the top of the bar above the apple. Trace the line to the left to see how many students chose apples. Your finger should land on the 2. So, 2 of Janice's classmates chose apples as their favorite fruit.

Content Standards: P.1.2, P.1.4

Practice

Directions: Use the following information to answer Numbers 1 through 5.

Maya visited Pacific Park on the Santa Monica Pier. The bar graph below shows how many times she rode each ride.

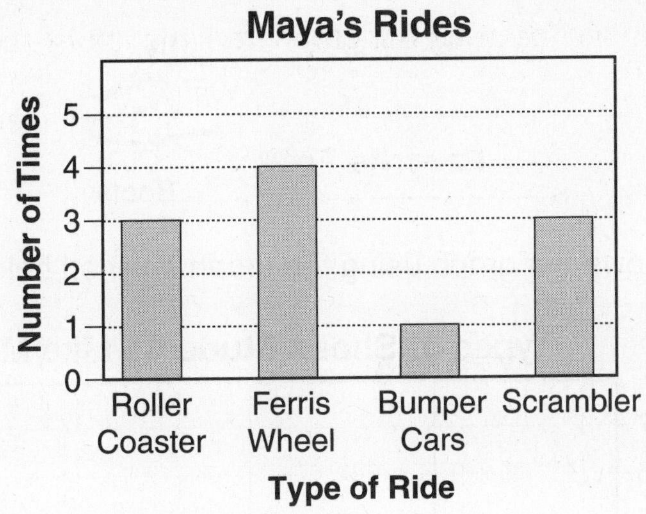

1. Which ride did Maya go on the **most**? ____________________

2. Which ride did Maya go on the **least**? ____________________

3. How many times did Maya ride the roller coaster? ________

4. How many more times did Maya ride the scrambler than the bumper cars?

   ____

5. How many times did Maya go on rides in all? ________

6. Ask your classmates which type of shoe they like to wear the most. Then record the numbers in the following spaces.

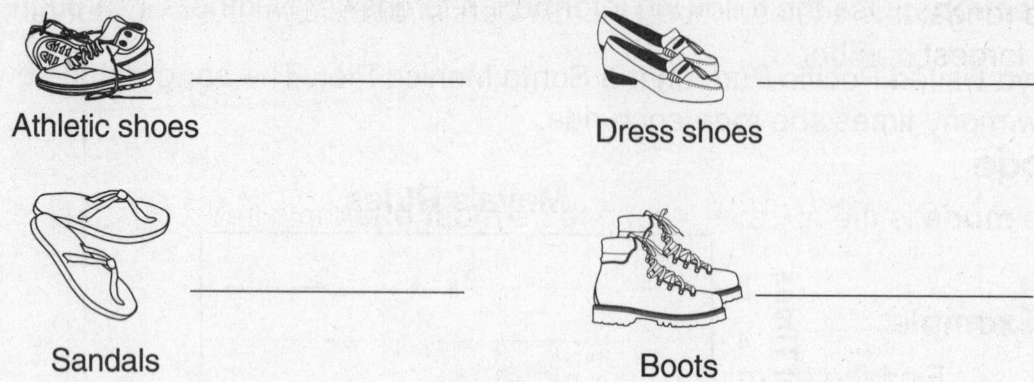

Now make your own bar graph using the graph outlined below.

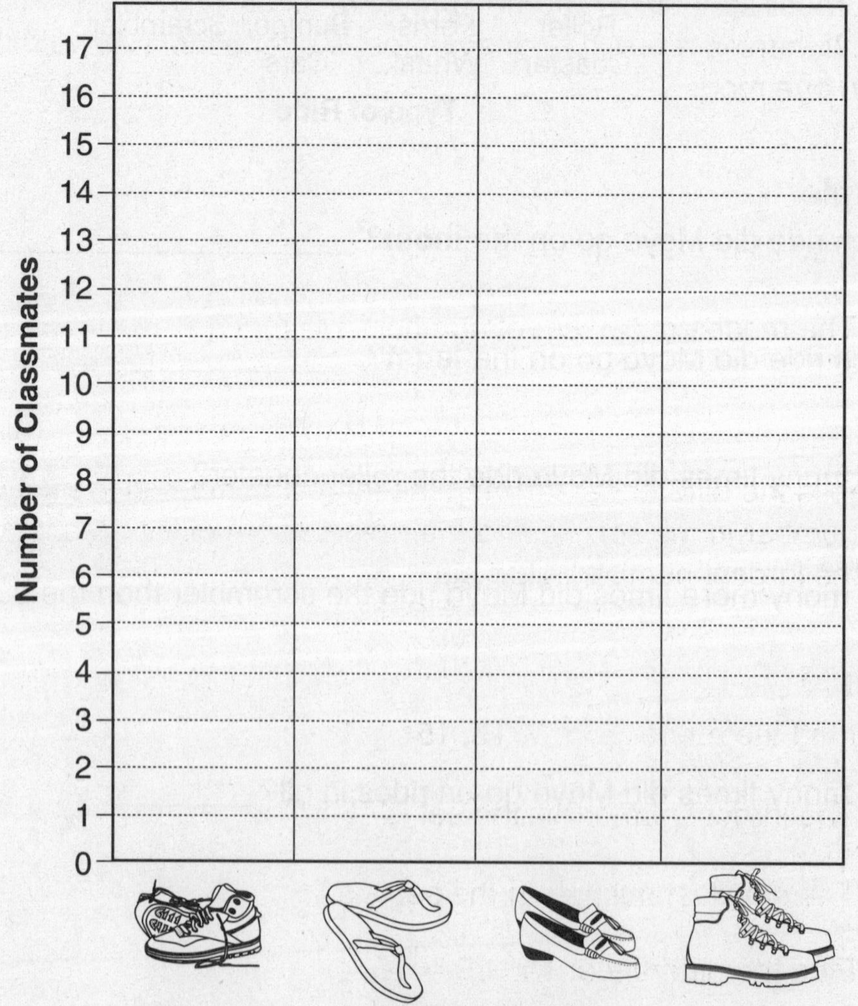

Content Standards: P.1.3

Mode and Range

Mode and range use a number to describe a set of numbers. To find the mode and range, it is easiest to put the numbers in order from the smallest number to the largest number.

Mode

The **mode** is the number that appears **most often** in a set of numbers.

Find the mode: 14, 15, **16**, **16**, 21

The mode of this set of numbers is 16.

If each number appears the same number of times in the set of numbers, there is no mode. If there is more than one number that appears most often, then there is more than one mode.

Find the mode: 3, 5, **6**, **6**, 7, **9**, **9**

The modes of this set of numbers are 6 and 9.

Range

The **range** is the difference between the largest number in the set and the smallest number in the set. To find the range, subtract the smallest number in the set from the largest number in the set.

Find the range: **5**, 6, 9, 15, **15**

The largest number in the set is 15.

The smallest number in the set is 5.

Find the difference: $15 - 5 = 10$.

The range of this set of numbers is 10.

Practice

Directions: Use the weights of the following cats to answer Numbers 1 through 3.

9 pounds

12 pounds

12 pounds

10 pounds

7 pounds

1. List the weights in order from the smallest weight to the largest weight.

   ____

2. What is the mode of the weights? __________

3. What is the range of the weights? __________

Directions: Use the following information to answer Numbers 4 through 6.

Mrs. Ericson measured each of her 5 children to see how tall they were.

Matthew: 60 inches	Carl: 52 inches	Jane: 48 inches
Liz: 63 inches	Beth: 54 inches	

4. List the heights in order from the smallest height to the largest height.

   ____

5. What is the mode of the heights? __________

6. What is the range of the heights? __________

Content Standards: P.1.3

Directions: Use the following information to answer Numbers 7 through 9.

Mirinda kept track of her spelling test score each week in the following table.

Spelling Tests

Week	Score
1	10
2	8
3	10
4	9
5	9
6	7

7. List the scores in order from the lowest score to the highest score.

____

8. What is the mode of the scores? __________

9. What is the range of the scores? __________

Directions: Use the following information to answer Numbers 10 through 12.

The list below shows Mario's score for each hole of goofy golf.

3, 2, 5, 4, 3, 6, 2, 3, 4

10. List the scores in order from the lowest score to the highest score.

____

11. What is the mode of the scores? __________

12. What is the range of the scores? __________

Practice Questions

1

Favorite Type of Music for Second Graders

Type	Tally	Count
Country	𝍸 III	8
Rock	𝍸	5
Blues	IIII	4
Pop	𝍸 II	7
Classical	II	2

3	4	5	7
Ⓐ	Ⓑ	Ⓒ	Ⓓ

2

Students' Favorite Colors

Red	
Yellow	
Blue	
Green	

12	8	6	4
Ⓐ	Ⓑ	Ⓒ	Ⓓ

3

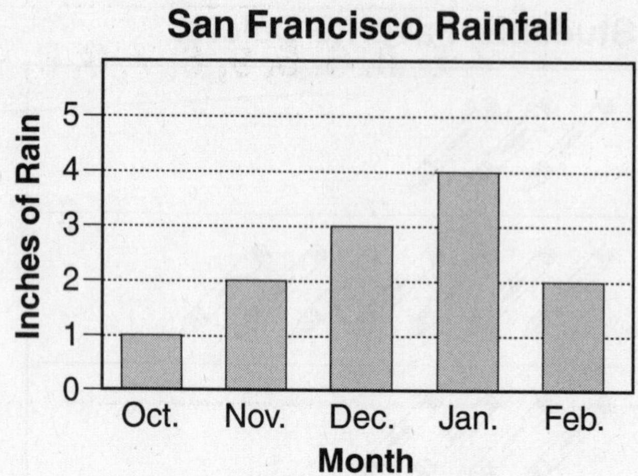

October and November Ⓐ	November and February Ⓒ
December and January Ⓑ	December and February Ⓓ

4

7, 5, 8, 6, 5, 9, 6, 7, 8, 8, 9

6 Ⓐ

7 Ⓑ

8 Ⓒ

9 Ⓓ

5

Books Read

Student	Books
Maria	10
Desmond	12
Victor	6
Ava	7
Lily	10

5 Ⓐ

6 Ⓑ

7 Ⓒ

10 Ⓓ

6

 **8**  **5** 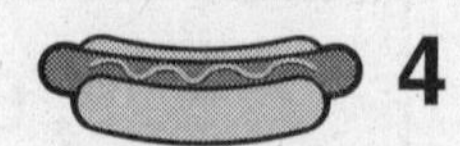 **4**  **6**

Favorite Foods

Food	Tally
Pizza	卌
Taco	卌 III
Hot dog	IIII
Hamburger	卌 I

Ⓐ

Favorite Foods

Food	Tally
Pizza	卌 III
Taco	IIII
Hot dog	卌
Hamburger	卌 I

Ⓒ

Favorite Foods

Food	Tally
Pizza	卌 I
Taco	IIII
Hot dog	卌
Hamburger	卌 III

Ⓑ

Favorite Foods

Food	Tally
Pizza	卌 III
Taco	卌
Hot dog	IIII
Hamburger	卌 I

Ⓓ